65p

UNIVERSITY MATHEMATICAL TEXTS
Founded by A. C. Aitken and D. E. Rutherford

EDITORS
ALAN JEFFREY, PH.D.
IAIN T. ADAMSON, PH.D.

Logic 223

Bic

36
PROBABILITY

D1437711

UNIVERSITY MATHEMATICAL TEXTS

PROBABILITY

JAMES R. GRAY, B.SC., F.F.A.

*Senior Lecturer in Statistics in the
University of St Andrews*

OLIVER & BOYD
EDINBURGH AND LONDON
NEW YORK: INTERSCIENCE PUBLISHERS INC.
A DIVISION OF JOHN WILEY & SONS, INC.

OLIVER AND BOYD LTD

Tweeddale Court
Edinburgh 1

39A Welbeck Street
London W.1

First edition 1967

Printed in Great Britain by
Robert Cunningham & Sons Ltd., Alva

CONTENTS

CHAPTER III

CONTINUOUS VARIATES

CHAPTER IV

OCCUPANCY, RUNS AND MATCHING

CHAPTER V

RECURRENCE RELATIONS FOR PROBABILITIES

ACKNOWLEDGEMENTS

This book is based on courses of lectures delivered at St Andrews University. I am indebted to *Introduction to Probability Theory* Vol. I by W. Feller for ideas on material and presentation and would thoroughly recommend this book to readers wishing to examine topics in greater detail.

I am grateful to the University of St Andrews and to the Faculty of Actuaries for permission to use examination questions as exercises. I wish to thank my colleagues R. L. Constable, P. D. L. Constable, C. D. Sinclair and Miss J. M. Kerr for useful suggestions and valuable assistance with exercises and proof correction.

Finally I must record my appreciation of the sustained interest, encouragement and patience shown by the late Professor Rutherford during the writing of this book, and of the help given at later stages by Dr Adamson.

J. R. GRAY

ST ANDREWS
August 1967

CHAPTER I

AXIOMS AND RESULTS

§1. Introduction. Everyone is familiar with situations in which the performance of some operation on a physical system results in one of a number of different possible outcomes where the particular outcome obtained is not under the control of the operator. The number of possible outcomes may be finite, enumerably infinite or non-enumerably infinite. Examples of operations with uncertain outcomes are tossing a coin, throwing a die, hitting a golf ball, finessing at bridge, making a speculative purchase on the Stock Exchange and answering the telephone.

The mathematical theory of probability should first provide a method of defining and identifying the probability of any specified outcome or "event" happening as the result of performing an operation or "trial" of the system. Secondly, probability calculus must define how probabilities of basic events are combined to give probabilities of more complex events.

Since mathematicians first became interested in the subject in the seventeenth century as the result of promptings by gamblers in France many attempts have been made to define probability formally. Philosophical and mathematical arguments have raged since then, but nowadays most people are prepared to accept the idea that the mathematical probability of an event is the theoretical equivalent of the "relative frequency" or proportion of occurrences of that event in a large number of independent repetitions of the trial.

Ideally it should be possible to deduce a measure of any probability from the description of the physical system and the trial, but this can only be achieved in special types of system where certain aspects of symmetry exist. These will be considered in §3. The fact that so many elementary problems relate to such systems tends, at times, to make us lose sight of their specialised nature.

In the general case we measure the probability, $p(E)$, of an event E on a scale from 0 to 1, i.e., $0 \leqslant p(E) \leqslant 1$. It can be verified experimentally that in those systems where repeated independent trials can be made, the relative frequency of E "converges" to a limit as the number of trials is increased. The form of this convergence is different from the standard idea of convergence to a limit in classical analysis and will be more fully discussed later. Meantime we can assume that there is this "stability" of relative frequency and regard the measure $p(E)$ as being the "limiting" value of the relative frequency of E.

In particular we see that impossible events will always have zero relative frequency and hence zero probability, while sure events will have unit relative frequency and hence unit probability. The converse of these statements is not true; the fact that the probability of an event E is 0 (or 1) does not necessarily mean that E is impossible (or certain) when the trial of the system has an infinite number of different possible outcomes.

It is important to appreciate that all probabilities cannot be assigned or identified in this way. There are many systems or situations in which repeated trials under identical conditions cannot be made. For example the probability that £100 of $3\frac{1}{2}\%$ War Loan will increase in value over the next six months cannot be assessed as the limit of relative frequency. Any measure of such probability is only some intuitive degree of belief which may differ considerably from person to person. There is no mathematical method of calculating these probabilities. However, once probabilities of this type have been assigned values, these can be combined according to the same laws or axioms which apply to mathematically assessed probabilities to obtain probabilities of combined events.

§2. Addition axiom for mutually exclusive events. The rules which govern the combination of probabilities are most easily presented in the form of unproved axioms. Their justification is the degree of agreement between practical relative frequencies of complex events and their probabilities calculated by using the axioms. It will be seen that proofs of the axioms in the case of systems allowing repeated independent trials are possible if we assume that relative frequency tends to a limiting value, probability, as the number of trials tends to infinity.

It is usual to regard all possible outcomes of a trial of a system as forming a set and to associate with an event E that subset of the set of all possible outcomes in which the event E happens. For example, if one card is picked from an ordinary pack of playing cards the set of possible outcomes is the set of all 52 possible different cards; if E is the appearance of a king, then the subset of outcomes associated with E would consist of the four cards, king of spades, king of hearts, king of diamonds, and king of clubs. Because of this, the union and intersection signs of set theory are used in probability theory. We use $E_1 \cup E_2$ to denote "at least one of E_1 and E_2", that is to say E_1 or E_2 or both E_1 and E_2, since $E_1 \cup E_2$ happens if any outcome belonging to the union of the subsets favourable to E_1 or E_2 respectively is obtained. By $E_1 \cap E_2$ we mean "both E_1 and E_2", and this happens if an outcome belonging to the intersection of the subsets favourable to E_1 and E_2 is obtained.

The first axiom is the **addition axiom** which in its simple form deals with mutually exclusive events. We consider a trial of some system where among the possible outcomes are two events E_1 and E_2 which cannot occur together, i.e., they are mutually exclusive. Then the simple addition axiom states:

If E_1 and E_2 are two mutually exclusive events, the probability that either E_1 or E_2 happens is the sum of their individual probabilities.

In symbols we have

$$p(E_1 \cup E_2) = p(E_1) + p(E_2).$$

The relative frequency justification for this axiom would be as follows. Suppose that in n repeated trials E_1 happened n_1 times and E_2 happened n_2 times; then E_1 or E_2 would happen $n_1 + n_2$ times and so the relative frequency of $E_1 \cup E_2$ would be $\dfrac{n_1 + n_2}{n}$ which equals the sum of the individual relative frequencies of E_1 and E_2. Taking limits as n tends to infinity, the axiom follows provided each relative frequency does tend to the corresponding probability. We shall assume that the axiom also applies to systems for which a relative frequency argument is inapplicable.

By successive application of the two-event axiom we can state more generally:

If $E_1, E_2, \ldots, E_n$ is any finite set of mutually exclusive *events, the probability that one of them happens is the sum of their individual probabilities:*

$$p(E_1 \cup E_2 \cup \ldots \cup E_n) = \sum_{i=1}^{n} p(E_i).$$

§3. Systems with symmetry. In physical systems with defined symmetry it is quite logical and permissible to regard the different possible outcomes of a trial as being "equally likely events". For example if an ordinary six-sided die with faces numbered 1, 2, 3, 4, 5, 6 is defined to be symmetrical, then the appearance of any one face in a throw of the die is obviously just as likely as the appearance of any other face. The set of six possible outcomes of a throw is an example of a set of equally likely events.

When the outcome of a trial of such a symmetrical physical system is known to be one or other of a finite set of equally likely mutually exclusive events, no other outcome being possible, the probability of each outcome may be deduced by an application of the addition axiom. Suppose that there are n equally likely possible mutually exclusive events $E_1, E_2, \ldots, E_n$ associated with a trial of a system and that the trial must result in one of them; then

$$p(E_1 \cup E_2 \cup \ldots \cup E_n) = p(E_1) + p(E_2) + \ldots + p(E_n).$$

Since the events are equally likely, their probabilities must be equal, and since one of them must occur, $E_1 \cup E_2 \cup \ldots \cup E_n$ is a certain event with probability 1. Thus we have

$$p(E_1) = p(E_2) = \ldots = p(E_n),$$
$$p(E_1) + p(E_2) + \ldots + p(E_n) = 1,$$

from which it follows that

$$p(E_1) = p(E_2) = \ldots = p(E_n) = \frac{1}{n}.$$

If F is an event which happens if and only if any one of a set of m ($\leqslant n$) of the E_i happens, say $E_{i_1}, E_{i_2}, \ldots, E_{i_m}$, then we have

$$\begin{aligned}
p(F) &= p(E_{i_1} \cup E_{i_2} \cup \ldots \cup E_{i_m}) \\
&= p(E_{i_1}) + p(E_{i_2}) + \ldots + p(E_{i_m}) \\
&= \frac{1}{n} + \frac{1}{n} + \ldots + \frac{1}{n} \qquad (m \text{ terms}) \\
&= \frac{m}{n}.
\end{aligned}$$

This gives the rule which is used for calculating probabilities for events associated with such systems:

$$p(F) = \frac{\text{Number of equally likely mutually exclusive favourable outcomes}}{\text{Total number of equally likely mutually exclusive possible outcomes}}.$$

This is the basis of many problems in elementary probability which appear in general textbooks on algebra. The idea is easily understood, but the actual enumeration of the number of favourable and, to a lesser degree, the number of possible events is often tricky and requires clear systematic thinking which can be developed by practice. Standard algebra of permutations and combinations may cover this enumeration, but less orthodox methods requiring some ingenuity in applying familiar mathematics are sometimes necessary.

Example 1.1. If a card is picked at random from a pack of playing cards, what is the probability that it is an ace?

The phrase "at random" means that the card is considered to be selected in a way which ensures that no one card is more likely to be selected than any other card. Because of this, we are entitled to regard the 52 possible cards which might be selected as equally likely events. Of these, there are four which are favourable, the four aces. Thus,

$$p(\text{Ace}) = \tfrac{4}{52} = \tfrac{1}{13}.$$

Example 1.2. Three balls are drawn at random from a bag which contains three black and four white balls. What is the probability that two are black and one is white?

Number of equally likely possible cases
$$= {}^7C_3 = 35.$$

Number of equally likely favourable cases
$$= {}^3C_2 \times {}^4C_1 = 12.$$

Hence

$$p(\text{Two black and one white}) = \tfrac{12}{35}.$$

Example 1.3. A symmetrical coin is tossed four times. What is the probability of at least two heads?

Since each toss can result in one of two equally likely outcomes the total number of equally likely possible outcomes of four tosses is seen to be $2 \times 2 \times 2 \times 2 = 16$.

There are eleven favourable outcomes, namely,

HHHH, HHHT, HHTH, HTHH, THHH, HHTT,
HTHT, HTTH, THHT, THTH, TTHH.

So the required probability is $\tfrac{11}{16}$.

Example 1.4. If a symmetrical coin is tossed five times, what is the probability of three or more consecutive heads?

The total number of possible equally likely outcomes is 2^5, i.e., 32. To enumerate the favourable cases we consider first those cases in which the sequence of at least three consecutive heads starts with the first toss. There are four such cases, HHH followed by H or T, followed by H or T. Then there are two cases in which the sequence of at least three consecutive heads starts at the second toss, THHH followed by H or T.

To this must be added those cases in which the run of heads does not start until the third toss. There are two such cases, H or T followed by THHH.

The required probability is thus $\dfrac{4+2+2}{32} = \frac{1}{4}$.

Example 1.5. If the digits 1, 2, 3, 4, 5, 6, 7 are written down in any order, each possible order being equally likely, to form a seven-digit number, what is the probability that this number will be divisible by eight?

The total number of equally likely seven-digit numbers is 7! = 5040. To determine the number of favourable cases, some systematic enumeration must be made of those seven-digit numbers, included in the 5040 possible cases, which are divisible by eight. We observe that 1,000 and hence 10,000, 100,000 and 1,000,000 are all exactly divisible by eight and that 100, 10 and 1 leave respective remainders 4, 2 and 1 on division by eight. Hence when the seven-digit number *abcdefg* is divided by eight there will be a remainder of the form $4e+2f+g$ and thus we must enumerate the different possible values of *e*, *f* and *g* which make $4e+2f+g$ an exact multiple of eight.

These sets of values are

$g = 2, f = 1, e = 3, 5$ or 7 $g = 4, f = 2, e = 6$
$g = 2, f = 3, e = 4$ or 6 $g = 4, f = 6, e = 2$
$g = 2, f = 5, e = 1, 3$ or 7
$g = 2, f = 7, e = 4$ or 6

$g = 6, f = 1, e = 2$ or 4
$g = 6, f = 3, e = 1, 5$ or 7
$g = 6, f = 5, e = 2$ or 4
$g = 6, f = 7, e = 1, 3$ or 5

There are therefore 22 different favourable sets of values of e, f, g and since for each such set there are 4! different orders of the remaining four digits in positions a, b, c, d there must be $22 \times 4!$ favourable seven-digit numbers. Thus the required probability is $\dfrac{22 \times 4!}{7!} = \dfrac{11}{105}$.

§4. **Geometrical diagrams.** The evaluation of probability from the symmetry of a system can be extended to systems with an infinite number of mutually exclusive possible outcomes. While it is no longer possible to express probability as the ratio of the number of favourable cases to the number of possible cases, the basic idea of identifying probability as the ratio of some form of measure of favourable cases to the corresponding measure of possible cases is retained. These measures may be lengths, areas or volumes in geometrical diagrams.

Example 1.6. A point is chosen at random from the continuous interval $[a, b]$ where $a < b$. What is the probability that it lies in the continuous interval $[c, d]$ where $a \leqslant c < d \leqslant b$?

P B

Representing the interval $[a, b]$ on the x-axis we have that all values of x in the continuous interval $[a, b]$ are equally likely. Favourable outcomes are values of x in the continuous interval $[c, d]$ and taking "measure" as the length of the continuous interval we see that

$$p(c \leqslant x \leqslant d) = \frac{\text{Length of the favourable interval}}{\text{Length of the possible interval}} = \frac{d-c}{b-a}.$$

It is obviously only possible to define "measure" as length of interval when all points in the interval are equally likely to be selected.

Example 1.7. A straight line is divided at random into three parts. What is the probability that these three parts can be formed into a proper triangle?

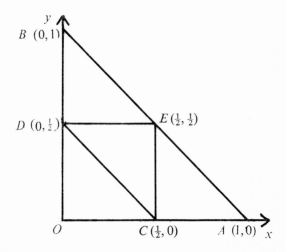

There is no loss of generality in taking the line to be of unit length. If we denote the length of the three parts by

x, y, $1-x-y$ then we see that any pair of values satisfying $0 \leqslant x \leqslant 1$, $0 \leqslant y \leqslant 1$, $0 \leqslant x+y \leqslant 1$ represents one of the possible equally likely cases of dividing the line. Representing these diagrammatically we see that all possible equally likely pairs of values of x and y are given by the points within triangle OAB.

Favourable pairs of values of x and y are those for which the sum of the lengths of any two parts is not less than the length of the third part. Thus favourable pairs must satisfy

$$x+y \geqslant 1-x-y, \text{ i.e., } x+y \geqslant \tfrac{1}{2}$$
$$x+1-x-y \geqslant y, \text{ i.e., } \quad y \leqslant \tfrac{1}{2}$$
$$y+1-x-y \geqslant x, \text{ i.e., } \quad x \leqslant \tfrac{1}{2}$$

and these are readily identified as the points lying in triangle DEC.

$$\text{Required probability} = \frac{\text{Area of } \triangle DEC}{\text{Area of } \triangle OAB} = \frac{1}{4}.$$

§5. Multiplication axiom for independent events. The second axiom used to combine probabilities is the **multiplication axiom** which, in its simple form, relates to what are known as independent events. Descriptively we can define two events as being independent if the probability that any specified one happens is unaffected by whether or not the other happens.

If E_1 and E_2 are two independent events the probability that both E_1 and E_2 happen is the product of their individual probabilities.

In symbols we have

$$p(E_1 \cap E_2) = p(E_1)\, p(E_2).$$

The relative frequency justification of this axiom would be as follows. Suppose that in n repetitions it was found that E_1 and E_2 occurred together n_{12} times, E_1 either with or without E_2 occurred n_1 times and E_2 either with or without E_1 occurred n_2 times. Then the relative frequency of both E_1 and E_2 is n_{12}/n while that of E_1 is n_1/n. Furthermore, the relative frequency of E_2 on those occasions on which E_1 happens is n_{12}/n_1 and since E_1 and E_2 are defined to be independent events, the limit of this relative frequency must be $p(E_2)$. Then, since $n_{12}/n = (n_1/n)(n_{12}/n_1)$, the axiom follows provided the relative frequences converge to the corresponding probabilities. We shall assume that the axiom also holds for events where relative frequency arguments are not applicable.

Repeated application of the two-event axiom leads to the more general result:

If $E_1, E_2, \ldots, E_n$ is any finite set of independent events, the probability that all events happen is the product of their individual probabilities:

$$p(E_1 \cap E_2 \cap \ldots \cap E_n) = \prod_{i=1}^{n} p(E_i).$$

In most cases the set of independent events arises as the result of a "trial" of a composite physical system which consists of making a set of trials of a number of independent component systems.

Example 1.8. If a symmetrical coin is tossed and a symmetrical six-sided die is thrown, what is the probability of heads and face number 6?

p(Heads and Number 6) $= p(H) \ p(6)$ since the events are clearly independent. So

$$p(H6) = \tfrac{1}{2} \cdot \tfrac{1}{6}$$
$$= \tfrac{1}{12}.$$

Example 1.9. If a symmetrical coin is tossed four times, what is the probability that heads appears each time?

$p(HHHH) = p(H) \ p(H) \ p(H) \ p(H)$ since the tosses are completely independent and hence the occurrence of heads at the different tosses are independent events. Thus

$$p(HHHH) = \tfrac{1}{2} \cdot \tfrac{1}{2} \cdot \tfrac{1}{2} \cdot \tfrac{1}{2} = \tfrac{1}{16}.$$

Example 1.10. If a symmetrical coin is tossed four times, what is the probability that heads appears exactly three times?

p(Exactly three heads)
   $= p(\text{HHHT} \cup \text{HHTH} \cup \text{HTHH} \cup \text{THHH}).$

Using the addition axiom for mutually exclusive events this is equal to

$$p(\text{HHHT}) + p(\text{HHTH}) + p(\text{HTHH}) + p(\text{THHH}).$$

Now by using the multiplication axiom we see that

required probability
$= p(H) \ p(H) \ p(H) \ p(T) + p(H) \ p(H) \ p(T) \ p(H) +$
$\quad p(H) \ p(T) \ p(H) \ p(H) + p(T) \ p(H) \ p(H) \ p(H)$
$= 4\{p(H)\}^3 p(T)$
$= 4 \cdot \tfrac{1}{8} \cdot \tfrac{1}{2}$
$= \tfrac{1}{4}.$

§6. Complementary event. When an event E does not happen as the result of a trial we say that the **complementary event** $\bar{E}$ has happened. Since E and $\bar{E}$ are mutually exclusive

$$p(E \cup \bar{E}) = p(\text{E}) + p(\bar{E}),$$

and further, since $E \cup \bar{E}$ is a sure event, with probability unity, it follows that

$$p(E) + p(\bar{E}) = 1,$$
$$p(E) = 1 - p(\bar{E}).$$

This relation is often useful in practice in providing a shorter method of evaluating a required probability. In any problem there is always the choice of calculating $p(E)$ or $p(\bar{E})$ and the simpler should always be selected.

Example 1.11. If a symmetrical six-sided die is thrown four times, what is the probability that at least one six appears?

Denoting by E the appearance of at least one six, direct evaluation would be

$$p(E) = p(\text{Exactly one six}) + p(\text{Exactly two sixes}) + $$
$$p(\text{Exactly three sixes}) + p(\text{Exactly four sixes}).$$

Each term on the right-hand side must be evaluated by the method of Example 1.10 and we obtain

$$p(E) = 4 \cdot \tfrac{1}{6}(\tfrac{5}{6})^3 + 6 \cdot (\tfrac{1}{6})^2(\tfrac{5}{6})^2 + 4 \cdot (\tfrac{1}{6})^3(\tfrac{5}{6}) + (\tfrac{1}{6})^4$$
$$= \tfrac{671}{1296}.$$

It is better to observe that $\bar{E}$ represents the appearance of no six.

$$p(\bar{E}) = p(\text{Not 6}) \, p(\text{Not 6}) \, p(\text{Not 6}) \, p(\text{Not 6}) = (\tfrac{5}{6})^4 = \tfrac{625}{1296}.$$
$$p(E) = 1 - p(E) = \tfrac{671}{1296}.$$

§7. Difference method. Some problems require the calculation of the probability that some quantity z is exactly equal to an integer k. In practice it is often easier to calculate the probability that z does not exceed k. From this, which is a function of k, the corresponding probability that z does not exceed $k-1$ is obtained on replacing k by $k-1$. Then since

$$p(z \leqslant k) = p(z \leqslant k-1 \cup z = k)$$
$$= p(z \leqslant k-1) + p(z = k),$$

we obtain the required probability as the difference between the two probabilities which have been calculated:

$$p(z = k) = p(z \leqslant k) - p(z \leqslant k-1).$$

Example 1.12. Ten tickets are numbered 1, 2, 3, ..., 10 respectively. Five tickets are selected one at a time with replacement. What is the probability that the highest number appearing on a selected ticket is k?

Probability that one ticket has a number $\leqslant k$ is $\dfrac{k}{10}$. Thus the probability that all five tickets have numbers $\leqslant k$ is $\left(\dfrac{k}{10}\right)^5$, i.e., the probability that the highest number on five selected tickets is $\leqslant k$ is $\left(\dfrac{k}{10}\right)^5$. Hence the probability that the highest number on five selected tickets is $\leqslant (k-1)$ is $\left(\dfrac{k-1}{10}\right)^5$.

Required probability $= \left(\dfrac{k}{10}\right)^5 - \left(\dfrac{k-1}{10}\right)^5$.

§8. Addition axiom for general events. The addition axiom can be stated in a more general form which applies to any events—the mutually exclusive condition being no longer necessary. Suppose that E_1 and E_2 are any two events. Then the probability that at least one of them happens must be the probability that (i) both E_1 and E_2 happen or (ii) E_1 happens but E_2 does not happen or (iii) E_1 does not happen but E_2 does happen; so

$$p(E_1 \cup E_2) = p((E_1 \cap E_2) \cup (E_1 \cap \bar{E}_2) \cup (\bar{E}_1 \cap E_2))$$
$$= p(E_1 \cap E_2) + p(E_1 \cap \bar{E}_2) + p(\bar{E}_1 \cap E_2),$$

since the three joint events are mutually exclusive.

It is common to omit the intersection symbol $\cap$ and write the probability that E_1 and E_2 both happen as $p(E_1E_2)$. With this modification we can write

$$p(E_1 \cup E_2) = p(E_1E_2) + p(E_1\bar{E}_2) + p(\bar{E}_1E_2) + $$
$$p(E_1E_2) - p(E_1E_2)$$
$$= p(E_1E_2 \cup E_1\bar{E}_2) + p(\bar{E}_1E_2 \cup E_1E_2) - $$
$$p(E_1E_2)$$
$$= p(E_1) + p(E_2) - p(E_1E_2)$$

since $p(E_1E_2 \cup E_1\bar{E}_2)$ denotes the probability that E_1 happens either along with E_2 or with $\bar{E}_2$ and thus is equal to $p(E_1)$.

Thus the **general two-event addition axiom** is:

If E_1 and E_2 are two general events, the probability that at least one of E_1 and E_2 happens is the sum of their individual probabilities diminished by the joint probability that they both happen.

The extended axiom for three events E_1, E_2, E_3 is obtained by a repeated application of the two event axiom. Let $F \equiv E_2 \cup E_3$.

$$p(E_1 \cup E_2 \cup E_3) = p(E_1 \cup F)$$
$$= p(E_1) + p(F) - p(E_1 F)$$
$$= p(E_1) + p(E_2 \cup E_3) - p(E_1 E_2 \cup E_1 E_3)$$
$$= p(E_1) + p(E_2) + p(E_3) - p(E_2 E_3) -$$
$$p(E_1 E_2) - p(E_1 E_3) + p(E_1 E_2 E_3)$$

since the joint probability of $E_1 E_2$ and $E_1 E_3$ is the same as the joint probability of E_1, E_2 and E_3.

The axiom for n general events E_1, E_2, ..., E_n can be established by induction and the two-event axiom, and is

$$p(E_1 \cup E_2 \cup \ldots \cup E_n) = \sum p(E_i) - \sum_{i<j} p(E_i E_j) +$$
$$\sum_{i<j<k} p(E_i E_j E_k) + \ldots + (-1)^{n-1} p(E_1 E_2 \ldots E_n),$$

where it should be remembered that $p(E_i E_j)$ is the total joint probability that E_i and E_j both happen irrespective of whether other events happen or not and similarly for the other terms on the right-hand side.

Since, when the events E_1, E_2, ..., E_n are mutually exclusive, all joint probabilities of two or more events must be zero, it is seen that the restricted addition axiom of §2 is a special case of the general addition axiom.

Example 1.13. The first n integers are written in random order, i.e., all permutations are equally likely. A match occurs in the rth position if the integer r is found to occupy that position. What is the probability that there is at least one such match?

The generalised addition axiom provides the solution to this classical problem of probability, sometimes described as the problem of "rencontres".

Let E_i denote the event that a match occurs in the ith position. Then

$p(E_i) =$
$\dfrac{(n-1)!}{n!}$ for $i = 1, 2, \ldots, n$, there being $\binom{n}{1}$ such terms.

$p(E_iE_j) = \dfrac{(n-2)!}{n!}$ for $i<j$, there being $\binom{n}{2}$ such terms.

$p(E_iE_jE_k) = \dfrac{(n-3)!}{n!}$ for $i<j<k$, there being $\binom{n}{3}$ such terms.

$\cdots \cdots \cdots \cdots \cdots \cdots \cdots$

$p(E_1E_2 \ldots E_n) = \dfrac{1}{n!}$, there being $\binom{n}{n}$ such terms.

Required probability $= p(E_1 \cup E_2 \cup \ldots \cup E_n)$

$$= n\frac{(n-1)!}{n!} - \frac{n!}{(n-2)!2!}\frac{(n-2)!}{n!} + \frac{n!}{(n-3)!3!}\frac{(n-3)!}{n!} - \cdots$$
$$\cdots + (-1)^{n-1}\frac{1}{n!}$$
$$= 1 - \frac{1}{2!} + \frac{1}{3!} - \frac{1}{4!} + \cdots + (-1)^{n-1}\frac{1}{n!}.$$

We note that as $n \to \infty$ this probability $\to 1 - e^{-1} = 0.632$.

§9. Multiplication axiom for general events.

Two events E_1 and E_2 are said to be dependent if the probability that one happens varies according to whether or not the other happens. The dependence can be recognised from the fact that the simple multiplication axiom does not then hold, i.e., $p(E_1E_2) \neq p(E_1)p(E_2)$.

Suppose one person is selected at random from a group of 200 persons known to conform to the following pattern of political views.

	Conservative	Labour	Liberal	Total
Men	30	50	20	100
Women	40	30	30	100
Total	70	80	50	200

If E_1 denotes the selection of a man and E_2 denotes the selection of a Liberal then by enumeration of favourable cases it follows that

$$p(E_1) = \tfrac{100}{200} = \tfrac{1}{2}, \; p(E_2) = \tfrac{50}{200} = \tfrac{1}{4}, \; p(E_1 E_2) = \tfrac{20}{200} = \tfrac{1}{10}.$$

We see that $p(E_1 E_2) \neq p(E_1) \, p(E_2)$, i.e., E_1 and E_2 are dependent and the probability that one happens is affected by whether or not the other happens.

For dependent events the concept of "conditional probability" must be introduced. We denote by $p(E_2 \mid E_1)$ the conditional probability that E_2 happens when it is assumed that E_1 happens. There are four conditional probabilities relating to two events E_1 and E_2: $p(E_2 \mid E_1)$, $p(E_2 \mid \bar{E}_1)$, $p(E_1 \mid E_2)$, $p(E_1 \mid \bar{E}_2)$. In our example these can be identified as

$$p(E_2 \mid E_1) = \tfrac{20}{100} = \tfrac{1}{5}, \qquad p(E_1 \mid E_2) = \tfrac{20}{50} = \tfrac{2}{5},$$
$$p(E_2 \mid \bar{E}_1) = \tfrac{30}{100} = \tfrac{3}{10}, \qquad p(E_1 \mid \bar{E}_2) = \tfrac{80}{150} = \tfrac{8}{15}.$$

From these values we see that

$$p(E_1 E_2) = p(E_1) \, p(E_2 \mid E_1) = p(E_2) \, p(E_1 \mid E_2).$$

This shows the more general form of the **multiplication axiom**:

If E_1 and E_2 are general events, the joint probability that they both happen is the product of the probability of E_1 and the conditional probability of E_2 when E_1 happens, or the product of the probability of E_2 and the conditional probability of E_1 when E_2 happens.

In symbols we have

$$p(E_1 E_2) = p(E_1)\, p(E_2 \mid E_1) = p(E_2)\, p(E_1 \mid E_2).$$

From this we can identify expressions for conditional probabilities:

$$p(E_2 \mid E_1) = \frac{p(E_1 E_2)}{p(E_1)} = \frac{p(E_2) p(E_1 \mid E_2)}{p(E_1)} \text{ provided } p(E_1) \neq 0;$$

$$p(E_1 \mid E_2) = \frac{p(E_1 E_2)}{p(E_2)} = \frac{p(E_1) p(E_2 \mid E_1)}{p(E_2)} \text{ provided } p(E_2) \neq 0.$$

In the case of independence,

$$p(E_1) = p(E_1 \mid E_2) = p(E_1 \mid \bar{E}_2)$$

and

$$p(E_2) = p(E_2 \mid E_1) = p(E_2 \mid \bar{E}_1),$$

so that the multiplication axiom for independent events is a particular case of the general multiplication axiom.

The multiplication axiom for n general events E_1, $E_2, \ldots, E_n$ takes the form

$$
\begin{aligned}
p(E_1 E_2 \ldots E_n) &= \\
&= p(E_1)\, p(E_2 \mid E_1)\, p(E_3 \mid E_1 E_2) \ldots p(E_n \mid E_1 E_2 \ldots E_{n-1}) \\
&= \text{Corresponding expressions for other orders of the } E_i
\end{aligned}
$$

where each conditional probability is calculated on the assumption that everything after the vertical line in the bracket happens.

Example 1.14. A bag contains three black and four white balls. Two balls are drawn at random one at a time without replacement. (i) What is the probability that the second ball selected is white? (ii) What is the conditional probability that the first ball selected is white if the second ball is known to be white?

(i) Let E_1 and E_2 represent respectively the events first and second ball white.

$$\begin{aligned}
p(E_2) &= p(E_1 E_2 \cup \bar{E}_1 E_2) \\
&= p(E_1 E_2) + p(\bar{E}_1 E_2) \\
&= p(E_1)\, p(E_2 \mid E_1) + p(\bar{E}_1)\, p(E_2 \mid \bar{E}_1) \\
&= \tfrac{4}{7} \cdot \tfrac{3}{6} + \tfrac{3}{7} \cdot \tfrac{4}{6} \\
&= \tfrac{4}{7},
\end{aligned}$$

where the values of the probabilities follow from simple enumeration—the conditional probabilities being calculated with reference to the six balls remaining after the first choice is made.

$$\begin{aligned}
\text{(ii)} \quad p(E_1 E_2) &= p(E_1)\, p(E_2 \mid E_1) \\
&= \tfrac{4}{7} \cdot \tfrac{3}{6} \\
&= \tfrac{2}{7}.
\end{aligned}$$

Hence

$$p(E_1 \mid E_2) = \frac{p(E_1 E_2)}{p(E_2)} = \tfrac{1}{2}.$$

§10. Bayes' formula.

The concept and properties of conditional probability lead to a useful result—Bayes' formula—which is used to modify probabilities in the light of additional relevant evidence.

We have seen that, for any two events A and B,

$$p(AB) = p(A)\, p(B \mid A) = p(B)\, p(A \mid B)$$

and hence that, provided $p(B) \neq 0$,

$$p(A \mid B) = \frac{p(A)\, p(B \mid A)}{p(B)} \quad \text{for all } A.$$

Suppose now that B is an event which can only occur in

conjunction with one of m mutually exclusive events C_1, C_2, ..., C_m and let us write

$$p(C_i) = p_i, \quad p(B \mid C_i) = \pi_i, \quad i = 1, 2, \ldots, m.$$

In these circumstances

$$p(B) = p(C_1 B \cup C_2 B \cup \ldots \cup C_m B)$$
$$= p(C_1 B) + p(C_2 B) + \ldots + p(C_m B)$$

(since the C_i are mutually exclusive)

$$= p(C_1) \, p(B \mid C_1) + p(C_2) \, p(B \mid C_2) + \ldots$$
$$\ldots + p(C_m) \, p(B \mid C_m)$$
$$= p_1 \pi_1 + p_2 \pi_2 + \ldots + p_m \pi_m.$$

Finally, replacing A by C_i it follows that

$$p(C_i \mid B) =$$
$$\frac{p(C_i) \, p(B \mid C_i)}{p(B)} = p_i \pi_i / (p_1 \pi_1 + p_2 \pi_2 + \ldots + p_m \pi_m).$$

This result is known as **Bayes' formula** or **Bayes' theorem** and provides an expression for the probability of C_i conditional on B in terms of the sets of probabilities $p(C_i)$ and $p(B \mid C_i)$. Its use is in the following type of situation.

The outcome of a trial of some system is observed to be the event B. This event could only happen if the system in which the trial was made was one of the mutually exclusive systems C_1, C_2, ..., C_m. Prior to making the trial, it was known that the respective initial or *a priori* probabilities of the system being C_1, C_2, ..., C_m were $p(C_1) = p_1$, $p(C_2) = p_2$, ..., $p(C_m) = p_m$. Once the trial has been performed and found to result in B we have additional information and we wish to reassess the respective probabilities of the C_i in the light of this new evidence, i.e., we wish to make a more up-to-date assessment of the probabilities of the C_i and replace the *a priori* probabilities which were based only on information available before the trial by *a posteriori* probabilities based on this information and the additional known fact that B occurs.

This type of problem is described as inverse probability. In previous examples we have been concerned with the calculation of probabilities of events at trials of uniquely known systems. In inverse probability the description of the physical system is uncertain. We observe that a particular event happens and are concerned with modifying our initial ideas of the system in the light of this knowledge. Thus we are, in a sense, solving an inverse problem.

Scepticism about applications of Bayes' formula stems not from theoretical objections to the derivation of the formula but from doubts as to whether realistic *a priori* probabilities $p(C_i)$ are available. For those problems in which the $p(C_i)$ and the $p(B \mid C_i)$ are available, the method is perfectly sound.

Example 1.15. Three boxes contain lamp bulbs some of which are defective. The proportions defective in box C_1, box C_2 and box C_3 are respectively $\frac{1}{2}$, $\frac{1}{8}$ and $\frac{3}{4}$. A box is selected at random and a bulb drawn from it. If the selected bulb is found to be defective, what is the probability that box C_1 was selected?

Since the selection of a box is random the *a priori* probabilities must be

$$p(C_1) = p(C_2) = p(C_3) = \tfrac{1}{3}.$$

The observed event B is that the bulb selected at random from the chosen box is defective. The conditional probabilities are easily seen to be

$$p(B \mid C_1) = \tfrac{1}{2}, \ p(B \mid C_2) = \tfrac{1}{8}, \ p(B \mid C_3) = \tfrac{3}{4}.$$

Then, applying Bayes' formula,

$$p(C_1 \mid B) = \frac{p(C_1)p(B \mid C_1)}{p(C_1)p(B \mid C_1) + p(C_2)p(B \mid C_2) + p(C_3)p(B \mid C_3)}$$
$$= \frac{\frac{1}{3} \cdot \frac{1}{2}}{\frac{1}{3} \cdot \frac{1}{2} + \frac{1}{3} \cdot \frac{1}{8} + \frac{1}{3} \cdot \frac{3}{4}}$$
$$= \frac{4}{11}.$$

Thus the information that a defective bulb has been found gives the *a posteriori* probability of C_1 as $\frac{4}{11}$ compared to the *a priori* probability $\frac{1}{3}$.

§11. Probability of exactly t general events.

The general addition axiom provides an expression for the probability that at least one of a set of n general events happens. We now develop a systematic expression for the probability that exactly $t \leqslant n$ of these events happen; the result is sometimes attributed to Waring (1792) and described as **Waring's theorem**.

We start by using the fact that $E_1 E_2 \cup E_1 \bar{E}_2 \equiv E_1$, so that

$$p(E_1) = p(E_1 E_2 \cup E_1 \bar{E}_2) = p(E_1 E_2) + p(E_1 \bar{E}_2)$$

from which it follows that

$$p(E_1 \bar{E}_2) = p(E_1) - p(E_1 E_2).$$

This relation expresses a joint probability involving a complementary event in terms of joint probabilities which do not involve complementary events.

If we introduce the notation

$$p\{E_1(1 - E_2)\} = p(E_1) - p(E_1 E_2),$$

we can write

$$p(E_1\bar{E}_2) = p\{E_1(1 - E_2)\},$$

and it is easy to verify that the notation can be applied to general expressions and that, for example,

$$p(E_iE_j \ldots E_k\bar{E}_u\bar{E}_v \ldots \bar{E}_w) = \\ p\{E_iE_j \ldots E_k(1 - E_u)(1 - E_v) \ldots (1 - E_w)\}$$

which on expansion gives the required joint probability as a linear combination of joint probabilities which involve no complementary events.

We can now develop the expression for the probability that exactly t of the events $E_1, E_2, \ldots, E_n$ happen, where $t \leqslant n$. If exactly t events happen then the remaining $(n - t)$ must not happen; since the particular set of t which happen may be any one of $\binom{n}{t}$ mutually exclusive sets, the required probability must be the sum of $\binom{n}{t}$ joint probabilities of the type

$$p(E_{k_1}E_{k_2} \ldots E_{k_t}\bar{E}_{k_{t+1}}\bar{E}_{k_{t+2}} \ldots \bar{E}_{k_n})$$

where $k_1, k_2, \ldots, k_n$ is a permutation of the integers 1, 2, \ldots, n.

$$p(E_{k_1}E_{k_2} \ldots E_{k_t}\bar{E}_{k_{t+1}}\bar{E}_{k_{t+2}} \ldots \bar{E}_{k_n}) = \\ p\{E_{k_1}E_{k_2} \ldots E_{k_t}(1 - E_{k_{t+1}})(1 - E_{k_{t+2}}) \ldots (1 - E_{k_n})\}$$

$$= p(E_{k_1}E_{k_2} \ldots E_{k_t}) - \sum_{i=t+1}^{n} p(E_{k_1}E_{k_2} \ldots \ldots E_{k_t}E_{k_i}) + \\ \sum_{\substack{i,\,j=t+1 \\ i<j}}^{n} p(E_{k_1}E_{k_2} \ldots E_{k_t}E_{k_i}E_{k_j}) + \ldots \\ \ldots + (-1)^{n-t}p(E_{k_1}E_{k_2} \ldots E_{k_t}E_{k_{t+1}} \ldots E_{k_n}).$$

In this expansion the number of joint probabilities relating to exactly $(t+u)$ of the events E_i is $\binom{n-t}{u}$ since there is one such term for each different set of u events from the $(n-t)$ events which appear as complementary events in the joint probability on the left-hand side.

Hence, in the required probability which is the sum of $\binom{n}{t}$ such expansions there are $\binom{n}{t}\binom{n-t}{u}$ joint probabilities relating to exactly $(t+u)$ events. Since there are only n events, there can be only $\binom{n}{t+u}$ distinct joint probabilities relating to $(t+u)$ events and therefore, by symmetry, each must occur $\binom{n}{t}\binom{n-t}{u} \Big/ \binom{n}{t+u} = \binom{t+u}{u}$ times in the final expansion for the required probability.

Writing S_{t+u} for $\sum p(E_{k_1} E_{k_2} \ldots E_{k_{t+u}})$, where the summation is over all $\binom{n}{t+u}$ different combinations of $(t+u)$ of the E_i, we finally have

$$p(\text{exactly } t \text{ events}) = \sum_{u=0}^{n-t} (-1)^u \binom{t+u}{u} S_{t+u}, \quad 0 \leqslant t \leqslant n.$$

In the case of $t = 0$, the summation includes the term S_0 which must be defined as 1.

By summing this probability for $t, t+1, \ldots, n$ we obtain

$$p(\text{at least } t \text{ events}) = \sum_{z=t}^{n} \left\{ \sum_{u=0}^{n-z} (-1)^u \binom{z+u}{u} S_{z+u} \right\},$$

which can be re-expressed in the form

$$p(\text{at least } t \text{ events}) = \sum_{u=0}^{n-t} (-1)^u \binom{t+u-1}{u} S_{t+u},$$

which holds for $0 \leqslant t \leqslant n$ provided we define S_0 as above and define $\binom{-1}{0}$ to be 1.

An important special case of these results arises when the events E_i are symmetrical in the sense that

$$p(E_1) = p(E_2) = \ldots = p(E_n),$$
$$p(E_1 E_2) = p(E_1 E_3) = \ldots = p(E_{n-1} E_n),$$
$$p(E_1 E_2 E_3) = p(E_1 E_2 E_4) = \ldots = p(E_{n-2} E_{n-1} E_n),$$

and so on. We then have

$$S_1 = \binom{n}{1} p(E_1),$$

$$S_2 = \binom{n}{2} p(E_1 E_2),$$

$$S_3 = \binom{n}{3} p(E_1 E_2 E_3), \ldots$$

If we denote by π_i the probability that $E_1, E_2, \ldots, E_i$ all happen, irrespective of whether the others happen or not, we can write

$$S_1 = \binom{n}{1} \pi_1, \quad S_2 = \binom{n}{2} \pi_2, \quad S_3 = \binom{n}{3} \pi_3, \ldots.$$

Then

$$p(\text{exactly } t \text{ events}) = \sum_{u=0}^{n-t} (-1)^u \binom{t+u}{u} \binom{n}{t+u} \pi_{t+u}.$$

Since $\binom{t+u}{u} \binom{n}{t+u} = \binom{n}{t} \binom{n-t}{u}$, this probability can be written in the form

$$p(\text{exactly } t \text{ events}) = \binom{n}{t} \sum_{u=0}^{n-t} (-1)^u \binom{n-t}{u} \pi_{t+u}.$$

From this, by summing over $t, t+1, \ldots, n$, it can be shown that

$$p(\text{at least } t \text{ events}) = \binom{n}{t}\sum_{u=0}^{n-t}(-1)^u\frac{t}{t+u}\binom{n-t}{u}\pi_{t+u}.$$

Example 1.16. If m objects are put into n cells each of which is large enough to contain all m objects should they fall into it and if each object is equally likely to fall into any cell, what is the probability that exactly t of the cells remain empty?

Let E_j denote the event that the jth cell is empty. Obviously the E_j form a symmetrical set so that $S_i = \binom{n}{i}\pi_i$.

Now π_i is the probability that i specified cells are empty, whether the others are empty or not, after the m objects have all been placed. The probability that a single object does not fall in any of those i cells is $\frac{n-i}{n}$ and hence the probability that m objects, all independently placed, do not fall in those cells is $\left(\frac{n-i}{n}\right)^m$ so that $\pi_i = \left(\frac{n-i}{n}\right)^m$. Hence

$$p(\text{exactly } t \text{ empty cells}) = \binom{n}{t}\sum_{u=0}^{n-t}(-1)^u\binom{n-t}{u}\frac{(n-t-u)^m}{n^m}$$

$$= \frac{1}{n^m}\binom{n}{t}\left\{(n-t)^m-\binom{n-t}{1}(n-t-1)^m+\binom{n-t}{2}(n-t-2)^m\right.$$

$$\left. + \ldots +(-1)^{n-t-1}\binom{n-t}{n-t-1}1^m\right\}$$

$$= \frac{1}{n^m}\binom{n}{t}\Delta^{n-t}0^m$$

where $\Delta^{n-t}0^m = [\Delta^{n-t}x^m]_{x=0}$ and Δ is the forward difference operator of finite difference calculus with unit intervals, defined by $\Delta f(x) = f(x+1) - f(x)$.

In particular, the probability that there will be no empty cell is seen to be $\dfrac{1}{n^m} \Delta^n 0^m$.

§12. Summary.

The formal rules of probability calculus are quickly summarised and easily remembered. We measure the probability of an event by a number in the interval [0, 1] which can be identified as the limiting value of a relative frequency, a degree of belief or for symmetrical systems a ratio of "measures" of favourable to possible equally likely outcomes. Probabilities are combined according to the addition and multiplication axioms. From these axioms, Bayes' formula and the results of §11 are developed to provide solutions for special classes of problems. It is also important to recall the possibility of calculating $p(\overline{E})$ as an alternative to calculating $p(E)$ directly and to realise the applications of the difference method.

Other specialised methods will be discussed later but most problems in probability calculus are solved by using only these results, together with any relevant tools of pure mathematics. It will be discovered, however, that these problems are far less stereotyped than those in many other branches of mathematics. It is essential to develop the ability to make systematic enumerations, a flexibility in restating problems and an initiative in solving them, all of which can only be achieved by the practical experience of working through many examples. There is no short cut to the attainment of proficiency and confidence in working with probability.

EXERCISES I

1. In four tosses of an unbiased coin, what are the probabilities of (i) three or more consecutive heads; (ii) heads exactly twice; (iii) heads at least twice?

2. An unbiased coin is tossed five times. What are the probabilities of (i) four or more consecutive heads; (ii) three or more consecutive heads?

3. Find the probability of a sequence of one or more tails followed by three or more consecutive heads in six tosses of an unbiased coin.

4. What is the probability of obtaining a sum of ten points in a throw of three symmetrical six-sided dice, each with faces numbered 1, 2, 3, 4, 5, 6?

5. Fifteen balls are distributed at random into five bags, three to each bag. What is the probability that two specified balls will be in the same bag?

6. A five-digit number is formed by writing the digits 1, 2, 3, 4, 5, in a random order. What is the probability that it is divisible by four?

7. Three tickets are chosen at random without replacement from a set of six tickets numbered respectively 1, 2, 3, 4, 5, 6; what is the probability that the sum of the numbers on the chosen tickets is 6?

If three tickets are similarly chosen from a set of twelve tickets numbered respectively 1, 2, . . . , 12, what is the probability that the sum of the numbers on the chosen tickets is 12?

If three tickets are similarly chosen from a set of $6n$ tickets numbered respectively 1, 2, . . . , $6n$, what is the probability that the sum of the numbers on the chosen tickets is $6n$?

8. Three tickets are drawn at random without replacement from a set of 100 tickets numbered respectively 1, 2, 3 . . . , 100. Find the probabilities that the numbers on the three chosen tickets can be arranged in (i) arithmetic progression; (ii) geometric progression.

9. A bag contains 120 similar counters of which 15 are numbered 1, 14 numbered 2, 13 numbered 3, . . . , two numbered 14 and one numbered 15. Three counters are drawn at random, one at a time with replacement. What is the probability that the sum of the three numbers drawn is either 35 or 40?

10. A sub-committee of six members is selected at random from the fifteen members of a committee, ten of whom are men and five women. Find the probabilities that the sub-committee (i) includes exactly five men; (ii) includes at least two women.

11. A straight line AB of unit length is divided internally at X where X is equally likely to be any point of AB. What is the probability that $AX \cdot XB < \frac{3}{16}$?

12. In the quadratic equation

$$x^2 + 2ax + b = 0,$$

a and b independently are equally likely to take any value in the interval from -1 to $+1$. Find the probability that the roots of the equation are real.

13. The sum of two positive quantities is known. If all pairs of possible values are equally likely, prove that the probability that their product will not be less than five-ninths of the maximum possible product is $\frac{2}{3}$.

14. If at a certain conference one of the delegates is equally likely to arrive at any time during an hour, find the probability that the greater of the times he was present or absent during that hour is at least n times the smaller.

If a second delegate is equally likely to arrive, independently, at any time during the same hour, what is the probability that the arrivals are separated by at least forty minutes?

15. A board is ruled by two sets of lines into a large number of squares of side l. Coins of radius r are rolled on to the board and fall at random. The owner of the board retains those which, on coming to rest, intersect a line, and returns, with a prize of an additional coin of the same value, those which do not intersect a line. What is the maximum value of l/r for which the owner can expect to make a profit?

16. If x and y independently are equally likely to take any value in the interval from 0 to 1, what is the probability that $x+y$ should be less than k (i) when $k < 1$; (ii) when $1 \leqslant k \leqslant 2$?

17. Two persons, A and B, make an appointment to meet on a certain day at a certain place, but without fixing the time further than that it is to be between 2 p.m. and 3 p.m. and that each is to wait not longer than ten minutes for the other. Assuming that each is independently equally likely to arrive at any time during the hour, find the probability that they meet.

A third person, C, is to be at the same place from 2.10 p.m. until 2.40 p.m. on the same day. Find the probabilities of C being present when A and B are there together (i) when A and B remain after they meet; (ii) when A and B leave as soon as they meet.

18. A business man is expecting two telephone calls. Mr Brown is equally likely to call any time between 2 p.m. and 4 p.m. while Mr Jones is equally likely to call any time between 2.30 p.m. and 3.15 p.m. Find the probabilities that:

(i) Mr Brown calls before Mr Jones;
(ii) the calls are less than ten minutes apart;
(iii) Mr Brown calls first, the calls are less than ten minutes apart and both are received before 3 p.m.

19. A straight line is divided at random into two parts and the larger of the two is sub-divided into two parts, again at random, so that the original line is now divided into three segments. Find the probability that the largest of the three is the middle one.

20. A straight line is divided at random into three parts. What is the probability that an acute-angled triangle can be formed by those three parts?

21. Assuming that the weather on any day is independent of that of the previous day and that the probability of rain on any day is $\frac{1}{2}$, find the probabilities that (i) it will rain either to-morrow or the next day; (ii) it will rain within a week.

22. The probability that A can solve a certain problem is $\frac{2}{5}$ and that B can solve it is $\frac{1}{3}$. If both try it, independently, what is the probability that it is solved?

23. A bag contains three white and two black balls. A player A gains a point whenever a ball drawn at random and replaced is white. When the ball drawn is black A loses all his points and B scores a point. Draws are continued until the game is won by the first player to reach a total of three points. Show that the probability that B leads A by

one point to zero is $1 - (3/5)^3$ and hence find the probability that A wins the game.

24. The respective probabilities of A and B winning a game are $\frac{4}{7}$ and $\frac{3}{7}$. If five independent games are played, find the probability that A wins three or more games in succession.

25. If n positive integers selected at random—repetitions being allowed—are multiplied together, find the probability that the final digit in their product is 5 and prove that this probability decreases as n increases.

26. An event E happens with probability $\frac{1}{3}$. Six independent trials are made. Find the probabilities of E happening (i) exactly twice; (ii) less than twice; (iii) more than twice.

27. Two tennis players A and B have respective probabilities $\frac{2}{5}$ and $\frac{3}{5}$ of winning any set. If they play five sets, what is the probability that A wins more sets than B?

What is the probability that the fifth set is the second set to be won by A?

28. Each second a particle α, which is constrained to move in a straight line, moves unit distance to the left or to the right with respective probabilities $\frac{1}{3}$ and $\frac{2}{3}$. Another particle β, starting from the same initial position and moving independently of α but in the same straight line, each second moves unit distance to the right or to the left with probabilities both equal to $\frac{1}{2}$. What is the probability that after five seconds β will be in a position to the right of α?

29. Three bags A_1, A_2, A_3 each contain r red balls and g green balls. A ball is drawn at random from each of A_1 and A_2. These two balls are interchanged and replaced.

A ball is then drawn at random from each of A_2 and A_3; these balls are then interchanged and replaced. If a ball is now drawn at random from A_3, what is the probability that it is red?

30. If A and B play a series of games in each of which the probability that A wins is p and that B wins is $q = 1-p$, obtain:
 (i) the probability that A wins two games before B wins three games;
 (ii) the probability that A is the first player to win two successive games.

31. A bag contains ten different cards and five cards are drawn at random with replacement. What are the probabilities that (i) all five cards are different; (ii) some card is drawn at least three times?

Find the minimum number of draws necessary to ensure a probability of at least $\frac{1}{2}$ that some card is drawn at least twice.

32. Two players A and B play a series of independent games. The respective probabilities of A and B winning any individual game are p and $q = 1-p$. If one player wins four games before the other wins three, he wins the series; otherwise play continues until one player has a lead of two games over his opponent, when he wins the series. Find the probabilities that:
 (i) the score reaches three games each;
 (ii) A wins the series with a total of four games;
 (iii) after the score has reached three games each, A wins the series.

33. Three students A, B and C independently make morning visits to a café. The probabilities that A, B, C go

on any given morning are $\frac{1}{2}$, $\frac{2}{3}$, $\frac{3}{4}$ respectively. Find the probabilities that, on any given morning, (i) all three go; (ii) exactly two go; (iii) only one goes; (iv) no one goes.

Find the probability that the total number of attendances in a five-day week is exactly five.

34. If two symmetrical six-sided dice, each numbered 1, 2, 3, 4, 5, 6 are thrown, what are the probabilities of obtaining:

(i)   at least one face showing 6;
(ii) a total of 6 from the two dice;
(iii) a total of 7 from the two dice.

The dice are thrown alternately by players *A* and *B*, *A* having the first throw. The game is won by *A* if he throws either at least one 6 or a total of 6 in one throw before *B* throws a total of 7 in one throw. Otherwise *B* wins the game. Find their respective probabilities of winning.

35. Is the occurrence of at least one 6 in four independent throws of a symmetrical six-sided die more probable than the occurrence of at least one double 6 in 24 independent throws of two such dice?

36. Assuming that birthdays are evenly distributed throughout the year and ignoring the extra day of leap years, find the probability that *n* people selected at random have different birthdays. Find the smallest value of *n* for which this probability is less than $\frac{1}{2}$.

37. A symmetrical six-sided die with faces numbered 1, 2, 3, 4, 5, 6 is thrown six times. Find the probabilities that:

(i) at least one of the numbers comes up at least twice;
(ii) at least two of the numbers do not come up at all.

38. A man draws a card at random from a pack of 52 playing cards. He then draws as many further cards from the remainder of the pack as the number on the card already drawn, ace counting one and king, queen and jack each counting ten. What is the probability that the ace of spades is among the cards drawn?

39. Three men, A, B, C have respective probabilities p, q, r of succeeding each time they attempt a certain task. They organise a competition with a prize for the first to succeed, each being allowed one attempt at a time in rotation in the order A, B, C, A, B, C, A, ... If under these conditions their chances of winning the prize are equal, express q and r as functions of p and hence show that $0 \leqslant p \leqslant \frac{1}{3}$.

Assuming p, q, r to satisfy these relations examine whether there are any possible values of p for which it would benefit B to support the proposal to reverse the order of attempts after each round so that attempts are made in the order A, B, C, C, B, A, A, B, C, C, ...

40. A certain kind of nuclear particle splits into 0, 1 or 2 new particles called descendants with respective probabilities $\frac{1}{4}$, $\frac{1}{2}$, $\frac{1}{4}$ and then dies. The individual particles act independently of one another. If x_1 denotes the number of descendants of a given particle, x_2 denotes the total number of the descendants of its descendants and x_3 denotes the total number of the descendants of the descendants of its descendants, find:

(i) the probability that $x_2 > 0$;
(ii) the conditional probability that $x_1 = 1$ given that $x_2 = 1$;
(iii) the probability that $x_3 = 0$.

41. A man is equally likely to choose any one of three routes A, B, C from his house to the railway station, and his choice of route is not influenced by the weather. If the weather is dry, the probabilities of missing the train by routes A, B, C are respectively $\frac{1}{20}$, $\frac{1}{10}$, $\frac{1}{5}$. He sets out on a dry day and misses the train. What is the probability that the route chosen was C?

On a wet day, the respective probabilities of missing the train by routes A, B, C are $\frac{1}{20}$, $\frac{1}{5}$, $\frac{1}{2}$. On the average one day in four is wet. If he misses the train what is the probability that the day was wet?

42. A university lecturer leaves his umbrella behind with probability $\frac{1}{4}$ every time he visits a shop. If he sets out, with his umbrella, to visit four different shops, what is the probability that he will leave it in the fourth shop? If he arrives home without his umbrella, what is the probability that he left it in the fourth shop? If he arrives home without it and was seen to be carrying it after leaving the first shop, what is the probability that he left it in the fourth shop?

43. The probabilities of four cricketers Brown, Green, White and Black scoring more than 50 runs in a match are $\frac{1}{2}$, $\frac{1}{3}$, $\frac{1}{4}$ and $\frac{1}{10}$ respectively. It is known that exactly two of these players scored more than 50 runs in a particular match. Find the probabilities (i) that these two players were Brown and Green; (ii) that one of these players was Brown; (iii) that Black scored more than 50 if it was also known that Brown did not score more than 50.

44. An ordinary symmetrical six-sided die is thrown four times and the sum of the four numbers thrown is 12. What is the probability that the sum of the numbers in the first two throws was 4?

45. A man chooses a painting at random from a group containing eight originals and two copies. He consults an expert whose chance of judging either an original or a copy correctly is $\frac{5}{6}$.

If the expert considers that the chosen painting is an original, what is the probability that this is so?

If the expert considers that the painting is a copy and the man returns it and chooses another painting at random from the other nine, what is the probability that this second painting is an original?

46. The stock of a warehouse consists of boxes of electric light bulbs. Forty per cent of the boxes contain bulbs of low quality for which the probability that any given bulb will prove satisfactory is $0{\cdot}8$; forty per cent contain bulbs of medium quality for which this probability is $0{\cdot}9$, and the remaining twenty per cent contain high quality bulbs which are certain to be satisfactory. If a box is chosen at random and two bulbs from it are tested, what is the probability that just one of the bulbs tested is satisfactory?

If it was found that just one of the bulbs tested was satisfactory, what is the probability that the selected box contained medium quality bulbs?

If both bulbs were found to be satisfactory, what is the probability that the selected box contained high quality bulbs?

47. A bag contains three balls each of which is black or white. A ball, drawn at random, is found to be white. Find the probabilities that it is the only white ball in the bag on the assumptions that initially either (i) it is equally likely that there are one, two or three white balls in the bag; or (ii) each ball is equally likely to be white or black.

If the drawn ball is replaced, what are the respective probabilities that the next ball drawn at random will be white?

48. One hundred bags each contain two balls. In 99 bags one ball is white and one ball is black; the hundredth bag contains two white balls. One bag is selected at random and a ball is drawn at random from it. What is the probability that this ball is white?

If the ball selected was found to be white, what is the probability that the other ball in that bag is also white? If the selected white ball was replaced and a second ball drawn at random from the same bag, what is the probability that this second ball is white?

If the procedure is repeated and it is found that n balls drawn at random with replacement from the same bag were all white, what is the probability that both balls in the selected bag are white? Find the smallest value of n for which this probability exceeds 0·95.

49. A bag contains five coins. Each coin can be either a shilling or a sixpence; all combinations are *a priori* equally likely. Two coins drawn at random without replacement are both found to be sixpences. If two further coins are drawn at random without replacement from the three now remaining in the bag, what is their expected† or average value?

50. It is known that in a bag containing a large number of counters, of which some are red and some blue, there are either twice as many red counters as blue or vice versa, these two possibilities being, *a priori*, equally likely. To test which is true, a man draws a counter at random from the bag, notes the colour and repeats the process. After

† See § 13.

six trials he concludes that it is four times as likely that the bag contains the larger number of blue counters as not. How many blue counters were obtained in these six trials?

Obtain the probability that, if he continues the trials, he will find his conclusion completely reversed after four more drawings, that is, that in the light of the results of all ten trials the bag is four times as likely to contain the larger number of red counters as not.

51. A department has eight members of staff. Their respective probabilities of remaining in employment in that department for three years are $\frac{2}{10}$, $\frac{3}{10}$, $\frac{4}{10}$, $\frac{5}{10}$, $\frac{6}{10}$, $\frac{7}{10}$, $\frac{8}{10}$, $\frac{9}{10}$. Find the probabilities that after three years (i) exactly six, and (ii) at least six of these members still work in the department.

52. A symmetrical six-sided die is thrown n times. What is the probability that no throw shows more than 4? What is the probability that the largest number obtained at any throw is 4?

Verify the results obtained for $n = 1, 2, 3, 4$.

53. Cards are drawn at random, one at a time with replacement, from an ordinary pack of playing cards. What is the probability that all four suits have appeared in the first n draws?

If cards are drawn until all four suits have appeared, deduce the probability that exactly n cards will be drawn.

54. Each month ten contracts are placed, each one at random at any one of the six branches of a company. Find the probability that in one month, all branches receive at least one contract.

What are the probabilities that in one month (i) exactly four branches and (ii) at least four branches receive at least one contract?

55. The population of a town is divided into three mutually exclusive strata, there being proportions $\frac{1}{8}$, $\frac{1}{4}$, $\frac{5}{8}$ of the total population in these respective strata.

A sample of eight members of the whole population is chosen at random, one at a time with replacement. Find the probability that at least one member from each stratum is included in the sample.

If the sample of eight members is known to include at least one member from each stratum, what is the conditional probability that members from all three strata were included for the first time after six members had been chosen?

56. Balls are drawn at random, one at a time with replacement, from a bag which contains one white, two black, three green and four red balls. Find the probability that at least one of the colours, white, black and green has not appeared after eight draws.

If it is known that at least one of these three colours has not appeared in eight draws, what is the conditional probability that exactly two have not appeared?

57. If the digits 1, 2, 3, 4, 5, 6 are written in random order, what is the probability that no digit is in its natural position?

How many permutations can be formed of the letters of the word A Z T E C S in which no letter is in its correct position?

58. An incompetent secretary has n letters and n corresponding addressed envelopes. If she puts the letters at random into the envelopes, one letter to each envelope, find an expression for the probability that exactly r letters are placed in wrong envelopes where $0 \leqslant r \leqslant n$.

Check the result obtained by examining the special cases $r = 0, 1, n$.

59. Each packet of a certain brand of detergent contains a numbered coupon, the number on any coupon being equally likely to be 1, 2, 3, 4, 5, 6, 7 or 8. Prizes are awarded to housewives who collect a set of coupons with all numbers showing. Obtain expressions for the probabilities that a housewife who buys twelve packets (i) obtains a prize; (ii) finds that exactly two numbers are missing.

60. A bag contains a proportion α of white balls, 2α of black balls and $(1 - 3\alpha)$ of red balls where $0 < \alpha < \frac{1}{3}$. Balls are drawn at random, one at a time with replacement. Find the probability that all colours appear for the first time at the nth draw.

Show that the probability of all colours appearing for the first time at the fourth draw is a maximum when $\alpha = \frac{2}{9}$.

CHAPTER II

INTEGRAL-VALUED VARIATES AND GENERATING FUNCTIONS

§13. Discrete variates. Mathematical statistics is concerned with the properties of **variates** or **random variables**. These are variables which take their different possible values according to some defined set of probabilities. There are two types of variate, discrete and continuous. In this chapter we shall only discuss discrete variates; continuous variates will be treated in the next chapter.

A **discrete variate** is a variable which can only take values belonging to some finite or infinite discrete enumerable set of real numbers, and for which there is a defined probability of taking any specified value. Moreover, the sum of all these probabilities is unity, that is to say, a variate is certain to take one of its possible values. The set of probabilities is the set of values of the associated **probability function**.

Suppose that the discrete variate is x and that its set of possible values is $x_1, x_2, x_3, \ldots$. The associated probability function $\phi(x)$ is defined by

$$\phi(x_i) = p(x = x_i), \quad i = 1, 2, 3, \ldots$$

all other values of $\phi(x)$ being zero. The probability function must satisfy the condition

$$\sum_{i=1}^{\infty} \phi(x_i) = 1.$$

For example, if x denotes the number of points obtained when a symmetrical die with faces numbered 1, 2, 3, 4, 5, 6 is thrown, the set of possible values would be $x_1, x_2, x_3, x_4, x_5, x_6$ where $x_i = i$ and the probability function would be defined by

$$\phi(x_i) = \tfrac{1}{6}, \quad i = 1, 2, 3, 4, 5, 6.$$

The two most important properties of any variate are its average value and its variability. The usual measure of average is the **arithmetic mean** which is defined by

$$\mu = \sum_{i=1}^{\infty} x_i \phi(x_i).$$

Thus μ is a weighted arithmetic average of the different possible variate values where the weights are the associated set of probabilities which add to unity. Alternative measures of average are defined in statistical textbooks but will not concern us. The arithmetic mean is also described as the **expected value** of the variate, and is denoted by $\mathscr{E}(x)$. More generally we define the expected value of any function $g(x)$ of the variate by

$$\mathscr{E}[g(x)] = \sum_{i=1}^{\infty} g(x_i) \phi(x_i).$$

Variability, or dispersion, is measured either by **variance** or by the square root of the variance which is called **standard**

deviation. The variance σ^2 is the expected value of the squared deviation of the variate from its arithmetic mean μ.

$$\begin{aligned}
\text{Variance} = \sigma^2 &= \mathscr{E}[(x-\mu)^2] \\
&= \sum_{i=1}^{\infty} (x_i-\mu)^2 \phi(x_i) \\
&= \sum_{i=1}^{\infty} x_i^2 \phi(x_i) - 2\mu \sum_{i=1}^{\infty} x_i \phi(x_i) + \mu^2 \sum_{i=1}^{\infty} \phi(x_i) \\
&= \sum_{i=1}^{\infty} x_i^2 \phi(x_i) - 2\mu.\mu + \mu^2.1 \\
&= \sum_{i=1}^{\infty} x_i^2 \phi(x_i) - \mu^2.
\end{aligned}$$

The standard deviation σ is the square root of this expression.

Most discrete variates of practical importance are integral-valued variates whose possible values are given by the set of positive integers, including the value 0. For these we write $p_i = p(x = i)$ where $i = 0, 1, 2, \ldots$, and we have

$$\sum_{i=0}^{\infty} p_i = 1, \quad \mu = \sum_{i=0}^{\infty} i p_i, \quad \sigma^2 = \sum_{i=0}^{\infty} i^2 p_i - \mu^2.$$

§14. Probability generating functions. If $a_0, a_1, a_2, \ldots,$ is a sequence of real numbers and if

$$A(s) = a_0 + a_1 s + a_2 s^2 + \ldots = \sum_{i=0}^{\infty} a_i s^i$$

converges in some interval $|s| < s_0$ where s is real, then $A(s)$ is called the **generating function** of the sequence $\{a_i\}$.

The variable s has no significance of its own and is introduced to identify a_i as the coefficient of s^i in the expansion of $A(s)$. When the sequence $\{a_i\}$ is bounded it is clear, by comparison with the geometric series, that $A(s)$ converges for $|s| < 1$.

In the particular case when a_i is the probability that an integral valued discrete variate x takes the value i, we have

$$a_i = p_i = p(x = i),$$

and we denote the generating function by $P(s)$ and define it to be the **probability generating function** of the variate x,

$$P(s) = \sum_{i=0}^{\infty} p_i s^i.$$

We can define a second sequence of probabilities $\{q_i\}$ for x by

$$q_i = p(x > i) = \sum_{j=i+1}^{\infty} p_j$$

and the corresponding generating function $Q(s) = \sum_{i=0}^{\infty} q_i s^i$. Since both $\{p_i\}$ and $\{q_i\}$ are bounded, the series $P(s)$ and $Q(s)$ certainly converge for $|s| < 1$. The function $Q(s)$ is not a probability generating function since the set of probabilities $\{q_i\}$ is not a discrete probability function.

We now prove three useful results concerning these generating functions:

(i) *For values of s for which both $P(s)$ and $Q(s)$ converge,*

$$(1-s)\, Q(s) = 1 - P(s).$$

The constant term on the left-hand side is q_0 which by

definition is equal to $1-p_0$ which is the constant term on the right-hand side.

The coefficient of s^j for $j \geqslant 1$ in $(1-s)Q(s)$ is q_j-q_{j-1}. Now

$$q_j - q_{j-1} = p(x > j) - p(x > j-1)$$
$$= -p(x = j)$$
$$= -p_j$$

and the result is proved by noting that this is the coefficient of s^j in $1-P(s)$.

(ii) *The arithmetic mean of x is given by*

$$\mu = P'(1) = Q(1)$$

where the dash denotes differentiation with respect to s. If $P'(s)$ and $Q(s)$ tend to infinity as s tends to 1 then μ is infinite.

If μ is finite, $P'(s) = \sum\limits_{i=0}^{\infty} ip_i s^{i-1}$ converges for $s = 1$ and $P'(1) = \sum\limits_{i=0}^{\infty} ip_i$ which, by definition, is μ.

Differentiation of the relation between $P(s)$ and $Q(s)$ established in (i) gives

$$(1-s)Q'(s) - Q(s) = -P'(s)$$

and, substituting 1 for s, $Q(1) = P'(1)$. Consequently,

$$\mu = P'(1) = Q(1).$$

It could also be shown from direct expansion of q_i in terms of $p_{i+1}, p_{i+2}, \dots$, that $\sum\limits_{i=0}^{\infty} q_i = \sum\limits_{i=0}^{\infty} ip_i$.

Obviously, if μ is infinite, $P'(s)$ and $Q(s)$ must tend to infinity when s tends to 1.

(iii) *If $\mathscr{E}(x^2)$ is finite, then*

$$\mathscr{E}(x^2) = P''(1) + P'(1) = 2Q'(1) + Q(1)$$

and hence

$$\sigma^2 = P''(1) + P'(1) - (P'(1))^2 = 2Q'(1) + Q(1) - (Q(1))^2.$$

σ^2 is infinite if $P''(s)$ and $Q'(s)$ tend to infinity as s tends to 1.

Since

$$\mathscr{E}(x^2) = \sum_{i=0}^{\infty} i^2 p_i = \sum_{i=0}^{\infty} i(i-1)p_i + \sum_{i=0}^{\infty} i p_i$$

and

$$P''(1) = \left\{ \sum_{i=0}^{\infty} i(i-1)s^{i-2}p_i \right\}_{s=1} = \sum_{i=0}^{\infty} i(i-1)p_i,$$

$$P'(1) = \sum_{i=0}^{\infty} i p_i,$$

when $\mathscr{E}(x^2)$ is finite the results in terms of $P''(1)$ and $P'(1)$ follow.

The equivalent expressions in terms of $Q'(1)$ and $Q(1)$ are obtained by differentiating the relation in (i) twice with respect to s and substituting $s = 1$.

Finally, since $\sigma^2 \geqslant 0$ it follows that it can only be infinite if $P''(s)$ and $Q'(s)$ tend to infinity as s tends to 1.

§15. Probability generating function for the sum of independent-variates. Convolutions.

If x and y are independent integral-valued discrete variates with respective probability generating functions $P(s) = \sum_{i=0}^{\infty} p_i s^i$ and $R(s) = \sum_{i=0}^{\infty} r_i s^i$ so that $p_i = p(x = i)$ and $r_i = p(y = i)$, it is possible to deduce the probability generating function for the variate $z = x+y$, which is also clearly integral-valued, in terms of $P(s)$ and $R(s)$.

Let w_k denote $p(z = k)$. The event $z = k$ can only happen as the result of the occurrence of some one of the mutually exclusive pairs of events $(x = 0, y = k)$, $(x = 1, y = k-1)$, $(x = 2, y = k-2), \ldots, (x = k, y = 0)$ and since the variates x and y are independent, each joint probability is the product of the appropriate individual probabilities. Furthermore, by the basic form of the addition axiom, the probability of some one of a number of mutually exclusive alternatives is the sum of the individual probabilities and so we have

$$w_k = p_0 r_k + p_1 r_{k-1} + p_2 r_{k-2} + \ldots + p_k r_0$$

for all integral $k \geqslant 0$.

The sequence of probabilities $\{w_k\}$ defined in terms of the sequences $\{p_k\}$ and $\{r_k\}$ is called the **convolution** of these sequences and is written

$$\{w_k\} = \{p_k\} * \{r_k\}.$$

The definition of convolution applies to any sequences $\{a_k\}$, $\{b_k\}$ and $\{c_k\}$ where $c_k = \sum_{i=0}^{k} a_i b_{k-i}$ for integral $k \geqslant 0$ and is not restricted to sequences of probabilities.

Since the coefficient of s^k in the product $P(s) \cdot R(s)$ can be identified as $p_0 r_k + p_1 r_{k-1} + \ldots + p_{k-1} r_1 + p_k r_0 = w_k$ it follows that the probability generating function for z, namely $\Omega(s) = \sum_{k=0}^{\infty} w_k s^k$, is equal to $P(s) \cdot R(s)$.

Thus we have the result that if x and y are independent

integral-valued discrete variates and if $z = x + y$, then the probability generating function for z is the product of the probability generating functions for x and y.

Repeated application of this result leads to the general result that if $x_1, x_2, \ldots, x_n$ are independent integral-valued discrete variates with respective probability generating functions $P_1(s), P_2(s), \ldots, P_n(s)$ and if $z = \sum_{i=1}^{n} x_i$, the probability generating function for z is given by

$$P_z(s) = \prod_{i=1}^{n} P_i(s).$$

In particular, when $x_1, x_2, \ldots, x_n$ all have the same probability function, and hence common probability generating function $P(s)$, we have

$$P_z(s) = [P(s)]^n.$$

Example 2.1. Four tickets are drawn, one at a time with replacement, from a set of ten tickets numbered respectively $1, 2, 3, \ldots, 10$, in such a way that at each draw each ticket is equally likely to be selected. What is the probability that the total of the numbers on the four drawn tickets is 20?

If x_i denotes the number on the ith ticket then, for $i = 1, 2, 3, 4$, we observe that x_i is an integral-valued variate with possible values $1, 2, 3, \ldots, 10$, each having associated probability $\frac{1}{10}$. Hence each x_i has probability generating function

$$\frac{1}{10}s + \frac{1}{10}s^2 + \frac{1}{10}s^3 + \ldots + \frac{1}{10}s^{10} = \frac{1}{10}s(1 - s^{10})(1 - s)^{-1}.$$

Then, since the x_i are clearly independent, it follows that the total of the numbers on the drawn tickets

$$z = x_1 + x_2 + x_3 + x_4$$

has probability generating function

$$\left\{ \frac{1}{10} s(1-s^{10})(1-s)^{-1} \right\}^4 = \frac{1}{10^4} s^4 (1-s^{10})^4 (1-s)^{-4}.$$

The required probability is the coefficient of s^{20} in this expansion, which is equal to the coefficient of s^{16} in

$$\frac{1}{10^4}(1-s^{10})^4(1-s)^{-4}$$

$$= \frac{1}{10^4}(1-4s^{10}+\dots)\left(1+4s+\frac{4.5}{1.2}s^2+\frac{4.5.6}{1.2.3}s^3+\frac{5.6.7}{1.2.3}s^4+\dots\right).$$

It follows that the required probability is

$$\frac{1}{10^4}\left\{\frac{17.18.19}{1.2.3.}-4\frac{7.8.9}{1.2.3}\right\} = \frac{633}{10,000}.$$

§16. Bernoulli binomial distribution. If a series of n independent trials is performed such that at each trial there is probability p that an event E happens and probability $q = 1-p$ that it does not happen, the total number of times, x, that the event happens, is an integral-valued variate. Its set of possible values is $0, 1, 2, \dots, n$ and its probability function is called the **Bernoulli binomial** (often just binomial) **probability function**.

We can deduce the values of the probability function from first principles. If $x = k$, there must be exactly k trials in which E happens and exactly $(n-k)$ in which E does not happen, the order being immaterial. Since the trials are independent, the joint probability of these results in one specified order is $p^k q^{n-k}$. There are $\binom{n}{k}$ mutually exclusive orders in which k E, and $(n-k)$ $\bar{E}$ can occur and so the probability that $x = k$ is the sum of $\binom{n}{k}$ joint probabilities each equal to $p^k q^{n-k}$.

Thus

$$p(x = k) = p_k = \binom{n}{k} p^k q^{n-k}, \quad k = 0, 1, 2, \ldots, n.$$

The arithmetic mean of the distribution is

$$\mu = \mathscr{E}(x) = \sum_{i=0}^{n} i p_i$$

$$= 0 \cdot q^n + 1 \cdot npq^{n-1} + 2 \cdot \frac{n(n-1)}{2!} p^2 q^{n-2} +$$

$$3 \cdot \frac{n(n-1)(n-2)}{3!} p^3 q^{n-3} + \ldots$$

$$+ (n-1) \cdot np^{n-1} q + n \cdot p^n$$

$$= np \left\{ q^{n-1} + (n-1)pq^{n-2} + \frac{(n-1)(n-2)}{2!} p^2 q^{n-3} \right.$$

$$\left. + \ldots + (n-1)p^{n-2}q + p^{n-1} \right\}$$

$$= np(q+p)^{n-1}$$

$$= np.$$

To find the variance, we must first evaluate

$$\mathscr{E}(x^2) = \sum_{i=0}^{n} i^2 p_i$$

$$= 0^2 \cdot q^n + 1^2 \cdot npq^{n-1} + 2^2 \cdot \frac{n(n-1)}{2!} p^2 q^{n-2}$$

$$+ 3^2 \cdot \frac{n(n-1)(n-2)}{3!} p^3 q^{n-3} + \cdots$$

$$+ (n-1)^2 np^{n-1} q + n^2 p^n$$

$$= np \left\{ q^{n-1} + 2(n-1)pq^{n-2} \right.$$

$$+ 3\frac{(n-1)(n-2)}{2!} p^2 q^{n-3} + \cdots$$

$$\left. + (n-1)(n-1)p^{n-2}q + np^{n-1} \right\}$$

$$= np \left\{ q^{n-1} + (n-1)pq^{n-2} + \frac{(n-1)(n-2)}{2!} p^2 q^{n-3} \right.$$

$$+ \cdots + (n-1)p^{n-2}q + p^{n-1}$$

$$+ (n-1)pq^{n-2} + 2\frac{(n-1)(n-2)}{2!} p^2 q^{n-3}$$

$$+ \cdots + (n-1)(n-2)p^{n-2}q$$

$$\left. + (n-1)p^{n-1} \right\}$$

$$= np \left\{ (q+p)^{n-1} + (n-1)p(q+p)^{n-2} \right\}$$

$$= np \left\{ 1 + np - p \right\}$$

$$= np \left\{ q + np \right\}.$$

Then we have

$$\sigma^2 = \mathscr{E}(x^2) - \mu^2 = npq + n^2p^2 - n^2p^2 = npq.$$

We can derive the binomial probability function and evaluate its arithmetic mean and variance much more easily by using generating functions and their properties. If we denote by y_i the number of times that E happens in the ith trial then y_i is an integral-valued variate with only two possible values, 0 and 1, which it takes with respective probabilities q and p. Thus the probability generating function of y_i is $(q+ps) = P_i(s)$ for $i = 1, 2, \ldots, n$. Since $x = \sum_{i=1}^{n} y_i$ and since the y_i must be independent variates as the trials are independent, by §15 the probability generating function for x is $P(s) = \prod_{i=1}^{n} P_i(s) = (q+ps)^n$.

The probability that $x = k$ is the coefficient of s^k in this expansion and is easily seen to be $\binom{n}{k}p^k q^{n-k}$ where $k = 0$, $1, 2, \ldots, n$. Using the results of §14 the arithmetic mean and variance are given by

$$\begin{aligned}
\mu &= P'(1) = np(q+p)^{n-1} = np, \\
\sigma^2 &= P''(1) + P'(1) - \{P'(1)\}^2 \\
&= n(n-1)p^2(q+p)^{n-2} + np - n^2 p^2 \\
&= npq.
\end{aligned}$$

§17. Poisson distribution. Another common integral-valued discrete distribution is the Poisson distribution. Here the variate x takes the possible values $0, 1, 2, 3, \ldots$ and for those values of x the probability function has the form $e^{-\lambda}\dfrac{\lambda^x}{x!}$, where $\lambda > 0$. Either from direct evaluation of $\mathscr{E}(x)$ and $\mathscr{E}(x^2)$ or by finding the probability generating function and differentiating as in §14, it is easy to show that the arithmetic mean and the variance of x are both equal to λ.

There is a whole family of Poisson variates, a specific member being defined by identifying the particular value of the parameter λ. We speak of the function

$$e^{-\lambda} \frac{\lambda^x}{x!}, \quad x = 0, 1, 2, 3, \ldots$$

as being the **Poisson probability function** with parameter λ, and describe x as being a **Poisson variate** with parameter λ. As we have seen, the value of the parameter is equal to both the arithmetic mean and the variance of the corresponding variate.

By using the compounding property of probability generating functions we can prove the following result:

If x_1 and x_2 are independent Poisson variates with respective parameters λ_1 and λ_2 then $z = x_1 + x_2$ is a Poisson variate with parameter $\lambda_1 + \lambda_2$.

The probability generating function for x_i $(i = 1, 2)$ is

$$P_{x_i}(s) = \sum_{j=0}^{\infty} e^{-\lambda_i} \frac{\lambda_i^j}{j!} s^j = e^{-\lambda_i} \sum_{j=0}^{\infty} \frac{(\lambda_i s)^j}{j!} = e^{-\lambda_i(1-s)}$$

and hence the probability generating function for z must be

$$P_z(s) = P_{x_1}(s) P_{x_2}(s) = e^{-(\lambda_1 + \lambda_2)(1-s)}$$

which is readily identified as the probability generating function for a Poisson variate with parameter $\lambda_1 + \lambda_2$.

This result can be extended to the sum of any finite number of independent Poisson variates.

The Poisson distribution can be regarded as a special limiting form of the binomial distribution in which n is large and p is small. To obtain this limit we must assume that we can write p in the form λ/n where λ is a positive finite constant and then take the limit of the binomial probability function as n tends to infinity.

The binomial probability of the variate value x is

$$\phi(x) = \binom{n}{x} p^x q^{n-x}$$
$$= \frac{n(n-1)(n-2)\ldots(n-x+1)}{x!} \left(\frac{\lambda}{n}\right)^x \left(1-\frac{\lambda}{n}\right)^{n-x}.$$

Thus

$$\underset{n\to\infty}{\mathrm{Lt}}\,\phi(x) = \frac{\lambda^x}{x!} \underset{n\to\infty}{\mathrm{Lt}} \left\{ \frac{n(n-1)(n-2)\ldots(n-x+1)}{n^x} \frac{\left(1-\dfrac{\lambda}{n}\right)^n}{\left(1-\dfrac{\lambda}{n}\right)^x} \right\}$$

$$= \frac{\lambda^x}{x!} \underset{n\to\infty}{\mathrm{Lt}} \left\{ \frac{1\left(1-\dfrac{1}{n}\right)\left(1-\dfrac{2}{n}\right)\ldots\left(1-\dfrac{x-1}{n}\right)}{\left(1-\dfrac{\lambda}{n}\right)^x} \left(1-\frac{\lambda}{n}\right)^n \right\}$$

$$= \frac{\lambda^x}{x!} e^{-\lambda}.$$

It can be verified that the Poisson probability function is a good approximation to the binomial whenever simultaneously n is fairly large and p is small, the corresponding Poisson distribution being that for which $\lambda = np$.

§18. Compound distributions. If $\{x_i\}$ is a sequence of independent integral-valued variates with common probability function, that is, for all i, $p(x_i = k) = p_k$, then the variate $y = \sum_{i=1}^{n} x_i$ where n is an integral-valued variate, independent of all the x_i, is said to have a compound distribution. It is obvious that y is also an integral-valued variate.

P E

Let the probability function for n be denoted by $p(n = k) = g_k$ for $k \geqslant 0$, and let its probability generating function be $G(s) = \sum_{k=0}^{\infty} g_k s^k$. Let the probability generating function for each x_i be $P(s) = \sum_{k=0}^{\infty} p_k s^k$.

By the basic addition and multiplication axioms we see that

$$p(y = j) = \sum_{k=0}^{\infty} p(n = k) \, p(\sum_{i=1}^{k} x_i = j)$$

$$= \sum_{k=0}^{\infty} g_k \, p(\sum_{i=1}^{k} x_i = j),$$

so that, if $Y(s)$ is the probability generating function for y, the coefficient of s^j in $Y(s)$ must be $\sum_{k=0}^{\infty} g_k \, p(\sum_{i=1}^{k} x_i = j)$. Now since the x_i are independent variates with common probability generating function $P(s)$, the probability that $\sum_{i=1}^{k} x_i = j$ for given k, is the coefficient of s^j in $[P(s)]^k$. Hence

$$p(y = j) = \text{coefficient of } s^j \text{ in } \sum_{k=0}^{\infty} g_k [P(s)]^k,$$

so that

$$Y(s) = \sum_{k=0}^{\infty} g_k [P(s)]^k.$$

Now, comparing the right-hand side with the definition of $G(s)$ it follows that

$$Y(s) = G[P(s)].$$

From $Y(s)$ we can obtain the values of the arithmetic mean and the variance from §14. Thus, remembering that $P(1) = \sum_{k=0}^{\infty} p_k = 1$, we have

$$\mu(y) = Y'(1) = G'[P(1)]P'(1)$$
$$= G'(1) \cdot P'(1)$$
$$= \mu(n) \cdot \mu(x).$$
$$\sigma^2(y) = Y''(1) + Y'(1) - [Y'(1)]^2$$
$$= G''[P(1)] [P'(1)]^2 + G'[P(1)]P''(1)$$
$$\quad + G'(1)P'(1) - [G'(1)]^2[P'(1)]^2$$
$$= \{G''(1) - [G'(1)]^2\} [P'(1)]^2 + G'(1) \{P''(1) + P'(1)\}$$
$$= \{\sigma^2(n) - \mu(n)\} \mu^2(x) + \mu(n) \{\sigma^2(x) + \mu^2(x)\}$$
$$= \mu^2(x) \sigma^2(n) + \mu(n) \sigma^2(x).$$

It should be noticed that the two basic properties of y have been evaluated without obtaining an explicit expression for its probability function.

Example 2.2. The number n of carriers of a disease in a certain district is a Poisson variate with parameter λ. The numbers of persons infected by different carriers are independent Poisson variates, each with parameter α. Find the probability generating function for the total number of persons infected, y, and hence obtain the arithmetic mean and the variance of this distribution.

If x_i denotes the number of persons infected by the ith carrier, then

$$P_i(s) = \sum_{k=0}^{\infty} e^{-\alpha} \frac{\alpha^k}{k!} s^k = e^{\alpha(s-1)} \text{ for } i = 1, 2, \ldots, n.$$

Moreover

$$G_n(s) = \sum_{k=0}^{\infty} e^{-\lambda} \frac{\lambda^k}{k!} s^k = e^{\lambda(s-1)}$$

and hence, since $y = \sum_{i=1}^{n} x_i$, we have

$$Y(s) = G[e^{\alpha(s-1)}] = \exp \lambda(e^{\alpha(s-1)} - 1).$$

Differentiating, we obtain

$$Y'(s) = \lambda\alpha e^{\alpha(s-1)} \exp \lambda(e^{\alpha(s-1)} - 1)$$

and

$$Y''(s) = \lambda^2\alpha^2 e^{2\alpha(s-1)} \exp \lambda(e^{\alpha(s-1)} - 1) \\ + \lambda\alpha^2 e^{\alpha(s-1)} \exp \lambda(e^{\alpha(s-1)} - 1),$$

so that

$$\mu(y) = Y'(1) = \lambda\alpha,$$

and

$$Y''(1) = \lambda^2\alpha^2 + \lambda\alpha^2,$$

from which it follows that

$$\sigma^2(y) = \lambda^2\alpha^2 + \lambda\alpha^2 + \lambda\alpha - \lambda^2\alpha^2 = \lambda\alpha(1+\alpha).$$

These values for $\mu(y)$ and $\sigma^2(y)$ could also have been obtained from substitution in the expressions obtained for them in terms of $\mu(x)$, $\sigma^2(x)$, $\mu(n)$, $\sigma^2(n)$ since $\mu(x) = \sigma^2(x) = \alpha$ and $\mu(n) = \sigma^2(n) = \lambda$.

§19. Chain distributions. A special application of the ideas of compound distributions arises in the study of populations whose members are capable of producing new members of like type. We shall refer to a member of the population as a particle. Any particle produces k new particles in the next generation with probability p_k, $k = 0$, 1, 2, ... where $\sum_{k=0}^{\infty} p_k = 1$. We start with a single particle in the original or zero generation; the $(n+1)$th generation consists of the total number of direct descendants of particles in the nth generation. The particles of each generation act independently of one another. The problem is to examine the properties of the probability distribution of the number of particles in the nth generation.

Let x_n denote the total number of nth generation particles. Then we see that

$x_0 = 1$ from the initial condition,

$x_1 = k$ with probability p_k, $k = 0$, 1, 2, ..., where $\sum_{k=0}^{\infty} p_k = 1$,

$x_2 = y_1 + y_2 + \ldots + y_{x_1}$ where each y_i has probability function p_k, and more generally,

$x_r = z_1 + z_2 + \ldots + z_{x_1}$, where z_i denotes the total number of $(r-1)$th generation descendants of the ith particle in the first generation and so each z_i has the same probability function as x_{r-1}.

Since the particles act independently, the y_i are independent variates and hence x_2 has the compound distribution with probability generating function

$$P_2(s) = P[P(s)] \quad \text{where} \quad P(s) = \sum_{k=0}^{\infty} p_k s^k.$$

Then since x_3 can be regarded as the total of the second generation descendants of the x_1 particles in the first generation each of which acts independently and produces a number of second generation descendants with probability generating function $P_2(s)$, x_3 has a compound distribution with probability generating function

$$P_3(s) = P[P_2(s)].$$

Similarly x_n consists of the total of the $(n-1)$th generation descendants of the x_1 first generation particles and has probability generating function

$$P_n(s) = P[P_{n-1}(s)].$$

While the explicit expansion of this probability generating function, and consequently the identification of the probability function for x_n, is seldom practicable, the recurrence relation for $P_n(s)$ enables recurrence relations to be obtained for $\mu(x_n)$ and $\sigma^2(x_n)$.

Denoting $\mathscr{E}(x_1) = \sum\limits_{k=0}^{\infty} k p_k$ by μ and $\sigma^2(x_1) = \sum\limits_{k=0}^{\infty} (k-\mu)^2 p_k$ by σ^2 we have

$$\mu = P'(1), \quad \sigma^2 = P''(1) + P'(1) - [P'(1)]^2.$$

Now

$$\begin{aligned} \mu(x_n) = P'_n(1) &= P'[P_{n-1}(1)]\, P'_{n-1}(1) \\ &= P'(1)\, P'_{n-1}(1) = \mu.\mu(x_{n-1}), \end{aligned}$$

and by repeated application of this reduction formula it follows that

$$\mu(x_n) = \mu^n.$$

Now $\qquad \sigma^2(x_n) = P''_n(1) + P'_n(1) - (P'_n(1))^2,$

and

$$\begin{aligned} P'_n(s) &= P'[P_{n-1}(s)]\, P'_{n-1}(s), \\ P''_n(s) &= P''[P_{n-1}(s)]\, (P'_{n-1}(s))^2 + P'[P_{n-1}(s)]\, P''_{n-1}(s), \\ P''_n(1) &= P''(1)\, (P'_{n-1}(1))^2 + P'(1)\, P''_{n-1}(1), \end{aligned}$$

so that

$$\begin{aligned}
\sigma^2(x_n) &= P''(1)\,(P'_{n-1}(1))^2 + P'(1)\,P''_{n-1}(1) \\
&\quad + \mu\,P'_{n-1}(1) - \mu^2(P'_{n-1}(1))^2 \\
&= (\sigma^2 + \mu^2 - \mu)\,(P'_{n-1}(1))^2 + \mu\,P''_{n-1}(1) \\
&\quad + \mu\,P'_{n-1}(1) - \mu^2(P'_{n-1}(1))^2.
\end{aligned}$$

Since $P'_{n-1}(1) = \mu^{n-1}$ it follows that

$$\begin{aligned}
\sigma^2(x_n) &= \mu\,\{P''_{n-1}(1) + P'_{n-1}(1) - (P'_{n-1}(1))^2\} + \sigma^2\mu^{2n-2} \\
&= \mu\,\sigma^2(x_{n-1}) + \sigma^2\mu^{2n-2}.
\end{aligned}$$

This is a first order linear difference equation with constant coefficients which can be solved by the standard methods discussed in Chapter V to give

$$\sigma^2(x_n) = \sigma^2\left\{\frac{\mu^{2n} - \mu^n}{\mu^2 - \mu}\right\} = \frac{\sigma^2\mu^{n-1}(\mu^n - 1)}{(\mu - 1)}.$$

Chain distributions are sometimes described as **branching processes**.

§20. Extinction probabilities for chain distributions.

A fundamental question to be examined for chain distributions is whether or not they "die out" before the nth generation. Clearly if there are no members of the nth generation, there is no possibility of there being any members of later generations. The two trivial cases (i) $p_0 = 0$ which means that the distribution can never die out, and (ii) $p_0 = 1$ which means that x_1 is certain to be 0, can be excluded from further consideration; we shall thus assume in what follows that $0 < p_0 < 1$.

Let ξ_n denote the probability that the distribution terminates at or before the nth generation. Then

$$\xi_n = p(x_n = 0) = P_n(0).$$

Now

$$\xi_{n+1} = p(x_1 = 0) + p(x_1 = 1)\,p(\text{No } n\text{th generation descendants of that particle})$$
$$+ p(x_1 = 2)\,p(\text{Each of these two independently acting particles has no } n\text{th generation descendants})$$
$$+ p(x_1 = 3)\,p(\text{Each of these three independently acting particles has no } n\text{th generation descendants})$$
$$+ \dots\dots\dots\dots\dots\dots\dots\dots\dots\dots\dots$$

Hence

$$\xi_{n+1} = p_0 + p_1\xi_n + p_2\xi_n^2 + p_3\xi_n^3 + \dots = P(\xi_n).$$

Alternatively this result could be derived directly from the recurrence relation for $P_n(s)$, since

$$\xi_{n+1} = p(x_{n+1} = 0) = P_{n+1}(0) = P[P_n(0)] = P(\xi_n).$$

As the coefficients of powers of s in the polynomial $P(s)$ are non-negative, being probabilities, we see that $P(s)$ is a monotonic increasing function of s.

Thus

$$\xi_2 = P(\xi_1) > P(0) = \xi_1$$

and hence by induction

$$\xi_{n+1} = P(\xi_n) > P(\xi_{n-1}) = \xi_n,$$

so that $\{\xi_n\}$ is a monotonic increasing sequence, as could have been inferred from general considerations.

Then, since ξ_n is a probability, the sequence $\{\xi_n\}$ is bounded and hence $\xi_n \to \xi$ where ξ must satisfy the equation

$$\xi = P(\xi).$$

Moreover this limiting probability ξ is the smallest positive root of this equation since if η is any other positive root,

$$\xi_1 = P(0) < P(\eta) = \eta.$$

Now if $\xi_n < \eta$ then $\xi_{n+1} = P(\xi_n) < P(\eta) = \eta$. Since $\xi_1 < \eta$, it follows by induction that all $\xi_n < \eta$, and hence that $\xi \leqslant \eta$.

If we make a more detailed examination of the roots of the equation $s = P(s)$ we see that $s = 1$ is always a root, and that if s_1 and s_2 are both roots then $\dfrac{P(s_2) - P(s_1)}{s_2 - s_1} = 1$ which, by the mean value theorem, implies $P'(s) = 1$ for some value of s in the interval (s_1, s_2). Now throughout $0 \leqslant s \leqslant 1$ the function $P'(s)$ is monotonic increasing and hence there exists at most one value of s in that interval for which $P'(s) = 1$. In other words, we see that there can exist at most one pair of roots, s_1 and s_2, of the equation which lie in the interval $0 \leqslant s \leqslant 1$. Since $s = 1$ is always a root, the necessary condition for the existence of a root in the interval $0 \leqslant s < 1$ must be that $P'(s) = 1$ for some $0 < s < 1$ which implies that $P'(1) > 1$. On the other hand, if no root $0 \leqslant s < 1$ exists, since $P(0) = p_0 > 0$ it follows that $P(s) > s$ for $0 \leqslant s < 1$. Since the function $P(s) - s > 0$ for $0 \leqslant s < 1$ and $P(1) - 1 = 0$ we must have $\dfrac{d}{ds}\{P(s) - s\} \leqslant 0$ when $s = 1$ so that $P'(1) \leqslant 1$.

Thus we have proved that a root $0 \leqslant s < 1$ of the equation $s = P(s)$ exists if and only if $P'(1) > 1$ and such a root is unique. Since $P'(1) = \sum_{k=0}^{\infty} k p_k = \mu$ we can state these results as follows.

If μ is the arithmetic mean of the number of direct descendants of a single particle, then when $\mu \leqslant 1$ the probability that the process will terminate before the nth generation, tends to 1 as n tends to infinity. When $\mu > 1$ there exists a unique root ξ of the equation $s = P(s)$ which satisfies the condition $0 \leqslant \xi < 1$, and ξ is the limit of the probability that the process terminates after a finite number of generations.

The value ξ is the **probability of extinction**; its complement $1 - \xi$ denotes the probability of an infinitely prolonged chain of descendants. In practice ξ_n tends quickly to ξ and so when $\xi = 1$, extinction is found to happen quite soon. Since $\mathscr{E}(x_n) = \mu^n$ we see that when $\mu > 1$, $1 - \xi$ is the limiting probability that the number of nth generation descendants exceeds any preassigned value as n tends to infinity.

§21. Use of recurrence relations in forming generating functions. When it is possible to form a recurrence relation between successive members in a sequence of probabilities it may be found that this leads to the most convenient derivation of the corresponding generating function.

Consider an infinitely prolonged sequence of independent trials with constant probability p of E happening and $q = 1 - p$ of $\bar{E}$ happening at any trial. Suppose we wish to find the generating function for the sequence $\{r_n\}$ where r_n denotes the probability that E has happened an even number of times in n trials, zero being regarded as an even number. We observe that

$r_n = p(either$ even number of occurrences in $(n-1)$ trials
    followed by non-occurrence at nth trial
    or odd number of occurrences in $(n-1)$ trials followed
    by occurrence at nth trial).

Hence

$$r_n = r_{n-1}q + (1-r_{n-1})p,$$

i.e., $r_n + (p-q)r_{n-1} = p$ for $n \geqslant 1$, where we must define $r_0 = 1$. If we multiply throughout this equation by s^n and sum all such resulting expressions for $n = 1, 2, 3, \ldots$ we obtain

$$\sum_{n=1}^{\infty} r_n s^n + (p-q)s \sum_{n=0}^{\infty} r_n s^n = p \sum_{n=1}^{\infty} s^n.$$

Then, since the required generating function is defined by

$$R(s) = \sum_{n=0}^{\infty} r_n s^n$$

and remembering that $r_0 = 1$, it follows that

$$R(s) - 1 + (p-q)s\, R(s) = \frac{ps}{1-s},$$

whence

$$R(s) = \frac{1-qs}{(1-qs+ps)(1-s)} = \tfrac{1}{2}\left\{ \frac{1}{1-qs+ps} + \frac{1}{1-s} \right\}.$$

Thus we have obtained an expression for $R(s)$ directly from the recurrence relation without first calculating explicit values for the probabilities $\{r_n\}$; these probabilities can be obtained by picking out coefficients in the expansion of $R(s)$. On the other hand, if it were only the probabilities $\{r_n\}$ that were required, they could be obtained more quickly by direct solution of the recurrence relation using the standard methods of Chapter V.

Since the sequence $\{r_n\}$ is not a set of probabilities of mutually exclusive events, $\sum_{n=0}^{\infty} r_n \neq 1$ and $R(s)$ is not a probability generating function for an integral-valued variate.

We now consider a second example in which the generating function derived is a proper probability generating function so that by using the results of §14 we can obtain the arithmetic mean and the variance of an integral-valued variate whose explicit probability function would be difficult to find.

Again a series of repeated independent trials, with respective probabilities p and $q = 1-p$ of E and $\bar{E}$ at any trial, is performed. The series is continued until an uninterrupted series of n consecutive occurrences of E is obtained and the variate x denotes the total number of trials required.

If $p_k = p(x = k)$ we see that

$$
\begin{aligned}
&p_k = 0, &&k = 0, 1, 2, \ldots, (n-1), \\
&p_k = p^n, &&k = n, \\
&p_k = qp^n, &&k = (n+1), (n+2), \ldots, 2n,
\end{aligned}
$$

$$
p_k = \{1 - \sum_{i=n}^{k-n-1} p_i\}qp^n, \quad k > 2n.
$$

The recurrence relation follows from the fact that the first uninterrupted run of n occurrences of E is completed at the kth trial provided no such run has been completed at any trial up to and including the $(k-n-1)$th, the $(k-n)$th trial resulted in $\bar{E}$ and all trials from $(k-n+1)$th to kth inclusive were successes.

Defining the probability generating function for the sequence $\{p_k\}$ by

$$
P(s) = \sum_{k=0}^{\infty} p_k s^k,
$$

which here is also equal to $\sum_{k=n}^{\infty} p_k s^k$, if we multiply each of the above equations for p_k by s^k and sum, we find

$$P(s) = p^n s^n + q p^n s^{n+1}(1+s+s^2+\ldots)$$
$$- q p^n s^{n+1}(1+s+s^2+\ldots)P(s),$$

whence

$$P(s) + \frac{q p^n s^{n+1}}{1-s} P(s) = p^n s^n + \frac{q p^n s^{n+1}}{1-s}$$
$$(1-s+q p^n s^{n+1})\, P(s) = p^n s^n - p^n s^{n+1} + q p^n s^{n+1}$$
$$= p^n s^n(1-ps),$$

and so finally

$$P(s) = \frac{p^n s^n(1-ps)}{1-s+q p^n s^{n+1}}.$$

To obtain the first and second derivatives of $P(s)$ necessary for the evaluation of the arithmetic mean and the variance of x, it is simpler to take logarithms and then differentiate.

$$\log P(s) = n \log p + n \log s + \log(1-ps) - \log(1-s+q p^n s^{n+1}),$$

whence

$$\frac{P'(s)}{P(s)} = \frac{n}{s} - \frac{p}{1-ps} + \frac{1-(n+1)q p^n s^n}{1-s+q p^n s^{n+1}}.$$

So, since $P(1) = 1$, it follows that

$$\mu(x) = P'(1) = \frac{1-p^n}{q p^n}.$$

Differentiating a second time we have

$$\frac{P''(s)}{P(s)} - \frac{(P'(s))^2}{(P(s))^2} =$$

$$-\frac{n}{s^2} - \frac{p^2}{(1-ps)^2} - \frac{n(n+1)qp^n s^{n-1}}{1-s+qp^n s^{n+1}} + \frac{\{1-(n+1)qp^n s^n\}^2}{\{1-s+qp^n s^{n+1}\}^2},$$

whence

$$\sigma^2(x) = P''(1) + P'(1) - (P'(1))^2 = \frac{1-p^{2n+1}-(2n+1)qp^n}{q^2 p^{2n}}.$$

§22. Partial fraction expansion of $P(s)$.

In general the explicit expansion of $P(s)$ and precise identification of the coefficients $\{p_k\}$ is not easy. It may however be possible to obtain approximate values for these coefficients. Suppose that $P(s)$ can be expressed in the form $P(s) = U(s)/V(s)$ where $U(s)$ and $V(s)$ are polynomials in s with no common factors and such that $U(s)$ is of lower degree than $V(s)$. We shall assume that $V(s)$ is of order n and that the n roots of the equation $V(s) = 0$ are the distinct values $s_1, s_2, \ldots, s_n$, so that

$$V(s) = (s-s_1)(s-s_2) \ldots (s-s_n).$$

Then from elementary algebra it is known that $P(s)$ can be expressed in the partial fraction form

$$P(s) = \frac{c_1}{s_1-s} + \frac{c_2}{s_2-s} + \ldots + \frac{c_n}{s_n-s},$$

where the numerators c_i are constants defined by

$$c_i = \frac{-U(s_i)}{V'(s_i)}, \quad i = 1, 2, \ldots, n.$$

Now since $\dfrac{1}{s_i - s}$ may be written in the form $\dfrac{1}{s_i}\left(1 - \dfrac{s}{s_i}\right)^{-1}$, then, provided $|s| < |s_i|$, we can expand this in the form $\displaystyle\sum_{k=0}^{\infty} \dfrac{s^k}{s_i^{k+1}}$. Expanding all terms in the above expression for $P(s)$ in this way we find that p_k, the coefficient of s^k in $P(s)$ is given by

$$p_k = \frac{c_1}{s_1^{k+1}} + \frac{c_2}{s_2^{k+1}} + \ldots + \frac{c_n}{s_n^{k+1}},$$

This expansion gives exact expressions for the sequence $\{p_k\}$ but to obtain it we required the complete solution of the nth degree equation

$$V(s) = 0,$$

which is usually a laborious process. When, however, this equation has one root s_i which is smaller in absolute value than all other roots, then for large values of k the probability p_k is given approximately by c_i/s_i^{k+1}, and this approximation only entails finding the one root of $V(s) = 0$ with smallest magnitude.

We notice that the method also applies when $V(s) = 0$ has multiple roots, provided s_i is a simple root. Also, of course, the result applies for rational functions with $U(s)$ of higher degree than $V(s)$ since $P(s)$ can then be expressed as the sum of a polynomial and a rational function of the previous form.

§23. Double generating functions. In solving certain problems it is useful to introduce the concept of double generating functions. These are secondary generating functions, whose coefficients are themselves generating functions. The idea is most easily understood by examining a problem where the technique is appropriate.

Two players A and B bet on the outcomes of a series of independent tosses of a symmetrical coin; A always bets on "heads" and B on "tails". We define A to be in the lead at any stage when the accumulated number of heads exceeds the accumulated number of tails or, when these totals are equal and A was leading after the previous trial. What is the probability that A is in the lead after each of exactly $2r$ out of a total of $2n$ trials?

Let $p_{2r:2n}$ denote the probability that A leads in exactly $2r$ out of $2n$ trials. For convenience we define $p_{0:0} = 1$ and observe that $p_{2r:2n} = 0$ if $r > n$ and if $r < 0$. We also define f_{2k} to be the probability that the accumulated numbers of heads and tails are equal for the first time after $2k$ trials. We require two properties of the sequence $\{f_{2k}\}$ which will be proved in Example (1) of §47. For the moment we must assume that $\sum_{k=1}^{\infty} f_{2k} = 1$ and that $F(s) = \sum_{k=1}^{\infty} f_{2k}s^{2k} = 1 - \sqrt{(1-s^2)}$.

Consider first the range of values $0 < r < n$. The overall outcome that A leads after exactly $2r$ of $2n$ trials can occur in the following mutually exclusive ways:

(i) First trial tails. First equalisation of accumulated scores at $2k$th trial ($k = 1, 2, \ldots, n$). A then to lead for $2r$ in the remaining $2n - 2k$ trials.

(ii) First trial heads. First equalisation of accumulated scores at $2k$th trial ($k = 1, 2, \ldots, n$). A then to lead for $2r - 2k$ in the remaining $2n - 2k$ trials.

Hence for $0 < r < n$ we can write

$$p_{2r:2n} = \tfrac{1}{2} \sum_{k=1}^{n} f_{2k} \, p_{2r:2n-2k} + \tfrac{1}{2} \sum_{k=1}^{n} f_{2k} \, p_{2r-2k:2n-2k}. \tag{1}$$

For $r = 0$ we see that (*ii*) can no longer make any contribution to $p_{2r:2n}$. There is, however, the new additional possibility of a first trial tails followed by no equalisation. The probability of this is

$$\tfrac{1}{2}(1 - f_2 - f_4 - \ldots - f_{2n}) = \tfrac{1}{2}\sum_{k=n+1}^{\infty} f_{2k}.$$

Hence for $r = 0$ we have

$$p_{0:2n} = \tfrac{1}{2}\sum_{k=1}^{n} f_{2k}\, p_{0:2n-2k} + \tfrac{1}{2}\sum_{k=n+1}^{\infty} f_{2k}. \tag{2}$$

For $r = n$ we similarly see that (*i*) makes no contribution to $p_{2r:2n}$ but that there is the possibility of first trial heads with no subsequent equalisation to be included. This probability is $\tfrac{1}{2}\sum_{k=n+1}^{\infty} f_{2k}$, so that for $r = n$ we have

$$p_{2n:2n} = \tfrac{1}{2}\sum_{k=1}^{n} f_{2k}\, p_{2n-2k:2n-2k} + \tfrac{1}{2}\sum_{k=n+1}^{\infty} f_{2k}. \tag{3}$$

Now multiply the equations (1) by s^{2r} where $0 < r < n$ and add to equation (2) and s^{2n} times equation (3). If we define $P_{2n}(s) = \sum_{r=0}^{n} p_{2r:2n} s^{2r}$ we obtain

$P_{2n}(s) =$

$$\tfrac{1}{2}\sum_{k=1}^{n} f_{2k} P_{2n-2k}(s) + \tfrac{1}{2}\sum_{k=1}^{n} f_{2k}s^{2k} P_{2n-2k}(s) + \tfrac{1}{2}(1 + s^{2n})\sum_{k=n+1}^{\infty} f_{2k}.$$

This is a recurrence relation between the probability generating functions for different total numbers of trials $2n$, and holds for $n = 0, 1, 2, \ldots$. If we multiply throughout by α^{2n}, sum the resulting equations for $n = 0, 1, 2 \ldots$ and

P F

define $P(s, \alpha)$ to be the double generating function

$$\sum_{n=0}^{\infty} P_{2n}(s)\alpha^{2n},$$

then, remembering that

$$\sum_{k=1}^{\infty} f_{2k}\alpha^{2k} = F(\alpha),$$

we have
$P(s, \alpha) =$

$$\tfrac{1}{2}P(s, \alpha)F(\alpha) + \tfrac{1}{2}P(s, \alpha)F(s\alpha) + \tfrac{1}{2}\sum_{n=0}^{\infty} \alpha^{2n}(1+s^{2n})\sum_{k=n+1}^{\infty} f_{2k}.$$

Now

$$\sum_{n=0}^{\infty} \alpha^{2n}(f_{2n+2}+f_{2n+4}+ \ldots)$$

$$= \sum_{k=1}^{\infty} f_{2k}(1+\alpha^2+\alpha^4+ \ldots +\alpha^{2k-2})$$

$$= \sum_{k=1}^{\infty} f_{2k}\frac{1-\alpha^{2k}}{1-\alpha^2}$$

$$= \frac{1-F(\alpha)}{1-\alpha^2} \quad \text{since} \quad \sum_{k=1}^{\infty} f_{2k} = 1.$$

Hence using the other assumed result, $F(\alpha) = 1-\sqrt{(1-\alpha^2)}$, we see that

$$\sum_{n=0}^{\infty} \alpha^{2n}(f_{2n+2}+f_{2n+4}+ \ldots) = 1/\sqrt{(1-\alpha^2)},$$

and similarly

$$\sum_{n=0}^{\infty} \alpha^{2n}s^{2n}(f_{2n+2}+f_{2n+4}+ \ldots) = 1/\sqrt{(1-\alpha^2s^2)}.$$

Thus we have the result

$$2P(s, \alpha) = \{F(\alpha) + F(s\alpha)\}P(s, \alpha) + (1-\alpha^2)^{-\frac{1}{2}} + (1-\alpha^2 s^2)^{-\frac{1}{2}}$$
$$= \{1 - (1-\alpha^2)^{\frac{1}{2}} + 1 - (1-\alpha^2 s^2)^{\frac{1}{2}}\}P(s, \alpha)$$
$$+ (1-\alpha^2)^{-\frac{1}{2}} + (1-\alpha^2 s^2)^{-\frac{1}{2}},$$

from which

$$P(s, \alpha) = (1-\alpha^2)^{-\frac{1}{2}}(1-\alpha^2 s^2)^{-\frac{1}{2}}.$$

Now the required probability $p_{2r:2n}$ is the coefficient of s^{2r} in $P_{2n}(s)$ and since $P_{2n}(s)$ is the coefficient of α^{2n} in $P(s, \alpha)$ the probability $p_{2r:2n}$ must be the coefficient of $\alpha^{2n}s^{2r}$ in the expansion of $P(s, \alpha)$. Thus we find

$$p_{2r:2n} =$$
$$\frac{(-1)^r}{r!}(-\tfrac{1}{2})(-\tfrac{3}{2})\dots\left(\frac{-2r+1}{2}\right)\frac{(-1)^{n-r}}{(n-r)!}(-\tfrac{1}{2})(-\tfrac{3}{2})\dots$$
$$\dots\left(\frac{-2n+2r+1}{2}\right) = \frac{1}{2^{2n}}\binom{2r}{r}\binom{2n-2r}{n-r}.$$

We observe that in the limit as both r and $(n-r)$ tend to infinity an approximation to $p_{2r:2n}$ can be found by using Stirling's approximation to the factorial,

$$n! \sim \sqrt{(2\pi n)}\left(\frac{n}{e}\right)^n.$$

We have

$$p_{2r:2n} \sim \frac{1}{2^{2n}}\frac{\sqrt{(4\pi r)}\left(\dfrac{2r}{e}\right)^{2r}\sqrt{\{4\pi(n-r)\}}\left(\dfrac{2n-2r}{e}\right)^{2n-2r}}{\left\{\sqrt{(2\pi r)}\left(\dfrac{r}{e}\right)^r\right\}^2\left\{\sqrt{\{2\pi(n-r)\}}\left(\dfrac{n-r}{e}\right)^{n-r}\right\}^2},$$

whence

$$p_{2r:2n} \sim \frac{1}{\pi\sqrt{\{r(n-r)\}}}.$$

The corresponding fraction of "time" that A leads is $\frac{r}{n}$ and for the limiting case we see that

$$p\left(a \leqslant \frac{r}{n} \leqslant b\right) = \sum_{a \leqslant \frac{r}{n} \leqslant b} \frac{1}{\pi} \frac{1}{\sqrt{\{r(n-r)\}}}$$

$$= \frac{1}{\pi} \sum_{a \leqslant \frac{r}{n} \leqslant b} \frac{1}{\sqrt{\left\{\frac{r}{n}(1-\frac{r}{n})\right\}}} \cdot \frac{1}{n}$$

$$\simeq \frac{1}{\pi} \int_a^b \frac{dx}{\sqrt{\{x(1-x)\}}}$$

$$= \frac{2}{\pi}(\text{arc sin } \sqrt{b} - \text{arc sin } \sqrt{a}).$$

In particular we observe that

$$p\left(0 \leqslant \frac{r}{n} \leqslant \tfrac{1}{2}\right) = \frac{2}{\pi} \text{ arc sin } \frac{1}{\sqrt{2}} = \tfrac{1}{2},$$

which we also obtain from general considerations of symmetry, and

$$p\left(\frac{r}{n} \leqslant t\right) = p\left(0 \leqslant \frac{r}{n} \leqslant t\right) = \frac{2}{\pi} \text{ arc sin } \sqrt{t}.$$

This is the **arcsine law** which describes certain fluctuating systems. It was first established in 1939 by Levy and has since been generalised by Erdös, Feller and Kac.

EXERCISES II

1. If x is any discrete variate and $y = ax+b$ where a and b are constants, prove that (i) $\mu_1'(y) = a\mu_1'(x)+b$; (ii) $\sigma^2(y) = a^2\sigma^2(x)$.

A variate y takes the values 23, 30, 37, 44, . . . , $16+7n$, each with probability $1/n$. Find its arithmetic mean and variance and hence prove that the average value of y^2 is

$$\tfrac{1}{6}(98n^2 + 819n + 2257).$$

2. If $z = x+y$, where x and y are independent discrete variates, show, by considering the relationship between the probability generating functions of the three variates, that (i) $\mu_1'(z) = \mu_1'(x)+\mu_1'(y)$; (ii) $\sigma^2(z) = \sigma^2(x)+\sigma^2(y)$.

3. A series of independent trials, each with probability p of success and $q = 1-p$ of failure is continued until a first success is obtained. If x denotes the number of trials required, show that the probability function for x is given by

$$\phi(x) = q^{x-1}p, \quad x = 1, 2, 3, \ldots.$$

Obtain its probability generating function and hence evaluate the arithmetic mean and the variance of x.

If, alternatively, trials are continued until the fifth success is obtained and if y denotes the total number of trials required, show that the probability function for y is given by

$$\psi(y) = \binom{y-1}{4} q^{y-5} p^5, \quad y = 5, 6, 7, \ldots.$$

4. Prove that the function

$$\phi(x) = (1+c)^{-k}\left(\frac{c}{1+c}\right)^x \frac{(k+x-1)!}{x!(k-1)!}, \qquad x = 0, 1, 2, 3, \ldots,$$

where c and k are positive constants, is a discrete probability function. Show that the arithmetic mean and the variance of x are respectively kc and $kc(c+1)$.

5. If a symmetrical six-sided die is thrown ten times, what is the probability that the total number of points obtained is 27?

6. The probabilities that a man will score 1, 0, -1 in any game are respectively $\frac{1}{4}$, $\frac{1}{2}$, $\frac{1}{4}$. Find the probability that his total score after n games is zero.

Each of two players tosses an unbiased coin n times scoring 1 for heads and 0 for tails on any toss. What is the probability that their total scores are equal?

7. The probability that an incompetent batsman scores x runs in an innings is

$$1/2^{x+1}, \qquad x = 0, 1, 2, \ldots.$$

What is the probability that he scores a total of five runs in six innings?

8. If x and y are independent Poisson variates each with mean value 1, calculate to two decimal places the probability that $x = y$ and hence find the probability that $x > y$.

9. If x is distributed according to the binomial distribution with probability function

$$\phi(x) = \binom{n}{x} p^x q^{n-x}, \qquad x = 0, 1, 2, \ldots, n$$

show that if z is the most probable value of x, then

$$\frac{z}{n+1} < p < \frac{z+1}{n+1}.$$

10. If $z = \sum_{i=1}^{n} x_i$ where the x_i are independent integral-valued variates with common probability function and n is an integral-valued variate distributed independently of the x_i prove that

$$\gamma(z) = \mu(n)\gamma(x) + \mu^3(x)\gamma(n) + 3\mu(x)\sigma^2(x)\sigma^2(n)$$

where μ, σ^2, γ denote respectively arithmetic mean, variance and third moment about the mean.

11. The number of seeds produced by any plant of a particular species is distributed according to a Poisson distribution with mean λ. Each seed independently does or does not produce a flower with respective probabilities p and $q = 1 - p$. If n initial plants are used where n has probability function

$$\phi(n) = \lambda q^n / n, \quad n = 1, 2, 3, \ldots$$

and where $p = e^{-1/\lambda}$, find the arithmetic mean and the variance of the total number of flowers produced by all the seeds of the n plants.

12. A population has initially a single member. Each member of any generation independently replaces itself by k members in the next generation where the probability function for k is

$$\phi(k) = \binom{2+k}{k}\left(\tfrac{2}{3}\right)^3\left(\tfrac{1}{3}\right)^k, \quad k = 0, 1, 2, \ldots.$$

Find the extinction probability for the population. Hence find the minimum initial population size to ensure an extinction probability of not more than 0·01.

13. The probability generating function for k, the number of members by which any member independently replaces itself in the next generation of a chain distribution is $\frac{1}{6}+\frac{1}{2}s+\frac{1}{3}s^2$.

If the population has a single initial member in the zero generation, what is the probability that the population dies out for the first time at the third generation?

If the initial population consists of r members, where r has probability function

$$\tfrac{1}{5}(\tfrac{4}{5})^{r-1}, \quad r = 1, 2, 3, 4, \ldots,$$

show that the probability of the population becoming extinct is $\frac{1}{6}$.

14. A series of independent trials with respective probabilities p and $q = 1-p$ of success or failure in a single trial is continued until an uninterrupted run of five consecutive successes is obtained. If x denotes the total number of trials performed, obtain its probability generating function and hence find the arithmetic mean and the variance of x.

15. A symmetrical six-sided die is thrown repeatedly. If u_n and v_n denote respectively the probabilities that the number six has appeared an odd and an even number of times in n throws, obtain the generating functions for the sequences $\{u_n\}$ and $\{v_n\}$ and hence verify that as n tends to ∞, u_n and v_n both tend to $\frac{1}{2}$.

CHAPTER III

CONTINUOUS VARIATES

§24. **Continuous variates.** A variable which can take any value in a continuous interval and which takes these different possible values according to a continuous probability density function is called a **continuous variate** or a **continuous random variable**. A rigorous treatment of continuous variates depends on the concepts of set and measure theory, and can be found in more advanced textbooks. We shall present the ideas in a less formal way which should make the manipulations plausible although they cannot be rigorously justified.

The **probability density function** of a continuous variate is a non-negative function $\phi(x)$ such that for any given pair of values a and b, such that $a < b$,

$$p(a \leqslant x \leqslant b) = \int_a^b \phi(x) \, dx.$$

It is common, although not strictly mathematical, to speak of $\phi(x) \, dx$ as representing the "element of probability" that the variate takes a value in the infinitesimal interval $(x, x+dx)$. Continuing in this intuitive manner, one can think of the probability of x lying in $[a, b]$ as being the probability that one or other of the mutually exclusive events, x lies in one of the non-overlapping infinitesimal intervals which make up $[a, b]$, should happen. If we now use the idea of the addition axiom in this wider context we can say

$$p(a \leqslant x \leqslant b) = \text{"Sum" of elements } \phi(x)\, dx = \int_a^b \phi(x)\, dx.$$

Analogous to the condition that $\sum_x \phi(x) = 1$ for a discrete variate, we now have $\int_{-\infty}^{\infty} \phi(x)\, dx = 1$ for continuous variates. The probability density function $\phi(x)$ is defined to be zero throughout those ranges in which x cannot take values, so that x can always be treated as having the theoretical interval of possible values $(-\infty, \infty)$ although its actual range may be of the type $(-\infty, k)$ or (k, ∞) or (k_1, k_2) where k, k_1, k_2 are any finite constants with $k_1 < k_2$.

The **arithmetic mean**, or **expected value**, of a continuous variate x is defined by

$$\mu = \int_{-\infty}^{\infty} x\phi(x)\, dx,$$

and its **variance** by

$$\sigma^2 = \int_{-\infty}^{\infty} (x-\mu)^2 \phi(x)\, dx$$

$$= \int_{-\infty}^{\infty} x^2 \phi(x)\, dx - \mu^2.$$

More generally, the **expected value** of any function $g(x)$ of a continuous variate x is defined by

$$\mathscr{E}[g(x)] = \int_{-\infty}^{\infty} g(x)\phi(x)\, dx.$$

The probability generating function $G(s) = \mathscr{E}(s^x)$ can be evaluated for continuous variates but is not found to be of much practical use. Unlike the case of the probability generating function for a discrete variate, there is no series expansion for a continuous probability generating function leading to the identification of required probabilities as coefficients of powers of s in this expansion. Other types of generating functions, for example moment generating functions and characteristic functions, are found to be useful in examining properties of continuous variates but they will not be considered here. Details can be obtained in any standard textbook on mathematical statistics.

§25. Examples of continuous variates.

Rectangular distribution

The simplest continuous distribution is the rectangular distribution in which the variate x is equally likely to take any value in the continuous interval $[0, 1]$ and cannot take any other values. The probability function is defined by

$$\phi(x) = \begin{cases} 1 & 0 \leqslant x \leqslant 1, \\ 0 & x \text{ not in } [0, 1]. \end{cases}$$

It can be seen that $\int_{-\infty}^{\infty} \phi(x)\,dx = \int_0^1 dx = 1$ and it is easy to show that $\mu = \frac{1}{2}$ and $\sigma^2 = \frac{1}{12}$.

A more general form of this distribution occurs where x is equally likely to take any value in $[a, b]$ where a, b are finite constants with $a < b$. Here $\phi(x) = \dfrac{1}{b-a}$ for $a \leqslant x \leqslant b$ and $\mu = \dfrac{b+a}{2}$, $\sigma^2 = \frac{1}{12}(b^2 - a^2)$.

Negative exponential distribution

A continuous distribution which occurs in mathematical models of queuing situations is the negative exponential distribution for which

$$\phi(x) = \lambda e^{-\lambda x}, \qquad 0 \leqslant x \leqslant \infty,$$

where λ is a positive constant. The basic properties are found to be $\mu = \dfrac{1}{\lambda}$, $\sigma^2 = \dfrac{1}{\lambda^2}$.

Gamma distribution

The gamma function $\Gamma(n)$ of a positive quantity n is defined by

$$\Gamma(n) = \int_0^\infty z^{n-1} e^{-z} dz$$

and it can be shown, by integrating by parts, that

$$\Gamma(n+1) = n\Gamma(n).$$

A continuous variate x is said to be distributed according to the gamma distribution with parameter n if its probability function is

$$\phi(x) = \frac{1}{\Gamma(n)} x^{n-1} e^{-x}, \qquad 0 \leqslant x \leqslant \infty.$$

From the definition of $\Gamma(n)$ it follows that

$$\int_{-\infty}^\infty \phi(x)\, dx = \int_0^\infty \frac{1}{\Gamma(n)} x^{n-1} e^{-x} dx = 1$$

and by using the recurrence relation it can be shown that $\mu = n$ and $\sigma^2 = n$.

Normal distribution

The standardised form of the normal probability function is

$$\phi(x) = \frac{1}{\sqrt{(2\pi)}} e^{-\frac{1}{2}x^2}, \qquad -\infty \leqslant x \leqslant \infty,$$

which can be shown to satisfy $\displaystyle\int_{-\infty}^{\infty} \phi(x)\,dx = 1$ and for which $\mu = 0$ and $\sigma^2 = 1$.

The general form of the normal probability function is

$$\phi(x) = \frac{1}{\sigma\sqrt{(2\pi)}} \exp -\tfrac{1}{2}(x-\mu)^2/\sigma^2, \qquad -\infty \leqslant x \leqslant \infty,$$

where again $\displaystyle\int_{-\infty}^{\infty} \phi(x)\,dx = 1$ and it can be verified that μ and σ^2 are the arithmetic mean and the variance of this distribution.

The integration necessary to establish these results requires further knowledge of the properties of integrals related to that which defines the gamma function.

§26. Truncated probability distributions. A variate can have a probability function which is proportional to that of another distribution but with its range of possible variate values restricted to a subset of the possible variate values of that distribution. For example the variate x might have a probability function proportional to the standardised normal distribution with the possible values of x restricted to $k \leqslant x \leqslant \infty$. Then the probability function for x would be of the form

$$\phi(x) = \begin{cases} c \dfrac{1}{\sqrt{(2\pi)}} e^{-\frac{1}{2}x^2} & k \leqslant x \leqslant \infty, \\ 0 & \text{for other values of } x, \end{cases}$$

and since $\displaystyle\int_{-\infty}^{\infty} \phi(x)\, dx = 1$, the constant c must be given by

$$c \int_{k}^{\infty} \frac{1}{\sqrt{(2\pi)}} e^{-\frac{1}{2}x^2} dx = 1.$$

Thus

$1/c = $ Probability that a standardised normal variate $\geqslant k$.

The variate x is said to be distributed according to a **truncated normal distribution**.

More generally we see that if $\phi(x)$ is the truncated probability function proportional to the probability function $f(x)$ and with variate values now restricted to the interval $[a, b]$ then

$$\phi(x) = \frac{f(x)}{\int_{a}^{b} f(x)\,dx} = \frac{f(x)}{F(b) - F(a)}, \qquad a \leqslant x \leqslant b,$$

where $F(x)$ is the distribution function corresponding to the probability function $f(x)$, and is defined by

$$F(x) = p(\text{Variate} \leqslant x) = \int_{-\infty}^{x} f(x)\,dx.$$

A truncated probability distribution can be regarded as a conditional probability distribution in the sense that if x has an unrestricted distribution with probability function $f(x)$ then $\phi(x)$ as defined above is the probability function which governs the behaviour of x subject to the condition that x is known to lie in $[a, b]$.

An interesting feature is found for a truncated form of the negative exponential distribution, $f(x) = \lambda e^{-\lambda x}, 0 \leqslant x \leqslant \infty$. Suppose that x is known to exceed a value k; then the truncated or conditional probability function is defined by

$$\phi(x) = \frac{\lambda e^{-\lambda x}}{\int_k^\infty \lambda e^{-\lambda x} dx} = \lambda e^{-\lambda(x-k)}, \quad k \leqslant x \leqslant \infty.$$

From this it follows that the conditional probability that $x \geqslant k + c$ when it is known that $x \geqslant k$ must be

$$p(x \geqslant k+c \,|\, x \geqslant k) =$$
$$\int_{k+c}^\infty \phi(x) dx = \int_{k+c}^\infty \lambda e^{-\lambda(x-k)} dx = e^{-\lambda c},$$

which is seen to be independent of k. Either by taking $k = 0$ in this result or by verifying that

$$\int_0^c f(x) dx = \int_0^c \lambda e^{-\lambda x} dx = e^{-\lambda c}$$

we establish the property that if x has a negative exponential distribution, then

$$p(x \geqslant k+c \,|\, x \geqslant k) = p(x \geqslant c).$$

Truncated distributions for discrete variates can be similarly defined.

§27. Continuous probability problems.

We have already seen in §4 how simple continuous probability problems can be solved by using suitable geometrical diagrams. That method, however, is only applicable when the concept of equal likeliness holds. More general problems involve continuous probability functions and their salient features are best presented by illustrative examples.

Example 3.1. The time x taken by a garage to effect a minor repair to a car is a continuous variate with probability function

$$\phi(x) = \tfrac{3}{4}x(2-x), \qquad 0 \leqslant x \leqslant 2.$$

Show that the probability of the repair taking more than time t where $0 \leqslant t \leqslant 2$ is

$$1 - \tfrac{3}{4}t^2 + \tfrac{1}{4}t^3.$$

If, on leaving his car, the motorist has an engagement lasting a time t where t is a continuous variate, independent of x, with probability function

$$\psi(t) = \tfrac{1}{2}t, \qquad 0 \leqslant t \leqslant 2,$$

what is the probability that the car will not be ready on his return?

$$\begin{aligned}
p(x \geqslant t) &= \int_t^\infty \phi(x)dx \\
&= \int_t^2 \tfrac{3}{4}x(2-x)dx \\
&= 1 - \tfrac{3}{4}t^2 + \tfrac{1}{4}t^3.
\end{aligned}$$

Since the simple multiplication axiom applies, the joint element of probability that the motorist returns in $(t, t+dt)$ and finds that the repair has not been completed is the product of $\psi(t)\,dt$ and $p(x \geqslant t)$. Thus

$$p\{\text{Return in } (t, t+dt) \text{ to find car not ready}\}$$
$$= (1 - \tfrac{3}{4}t^2 + \tfrac{1}{4}t^3)\tfrac{1}{2}t\,dt.$$

The total probability that the motorist returns to find the car not ready is the "sum" of all such mutually exclusive elements of joint probability for t taking values in the interval [0, 2].

Required probability $= \int_0^2 (1 - \tfrac{3}{4}t^2 + \tfrac{1}{4}t^3) \tfrac{1}{2}t \, dt = \tfrac{3}{10}$.

Example 3.2. The time t taken to serve a customer in a shop with a single server is a continuous variate with probability function

$$\phi(t) = \lambda e^{-\lambda t}, \qquad 0 \leqslant t \leqslant \infty, \qquad \lambda > 0,$$

and the time which elapses between the arrivals of the first and second customers is an independent continuous variate s with probability function

$$\psi(s) = \mu e^{-\mu s}, \qquad 0 \leqslant s \leqslant \infty, \qquad \mu > 0.$$

Assuming that there is only one customer, who has just arrived, being served, what is the probability that a second customer will arrive before closing time T to find the first customer still being served?

The probability that the first customer is still being served after time s is

$$p(t \geqslant s) = p(s \leqslant t \leqslant \infty) =$$
$$\int_s^\infty \phi(t) dt = \int_s^\infty \lambda e^{-\lambda t} dt = e^{-\lambda s}.$$

Hence the joint element of probability that the second customer arrives in $(s, s+ds)$ and finds the first customer still being served is

$$\psi(s) \, ds \, p(s \leqslant t \leqslant \infty) = \mu e^{-(\lambda+\mu)s} \, ds.$$

P G

The required probability is the "sum" of all such mutually exclusive joint elements for s taking values between 0 and T.

Required probability =

$$\int_0^T \mu e^{-(\lambda+\mu)s}\, ds = \frac{\mu}{\mu+\lambda}\{1 - e^{(\lambda+\mu)T}\}.$$

§28. Chebyshev's inequality.

If x is any variate, discrete or continuous, with arithmetic mean μ and standard deviation σ, the probability that x takes a value which differs from μ by more than $k\sigma$ is not greater than $1/k^2$, that is

$$p\{\,|\,x-\mu\,| > k\sigma\} \leqslant \frac{1}{k^2}.$$

We prove the result for a continuous variate with probability function $\phi(x)$; similar arguments establish the inequality for any discrete variate.

By definition,

$$\sigma^2 = \int_{-\infty}^{\infty} (x-\mu)^2 \phi(x) dx$$

$$= \int_{-\infty}^{\mu-k\sigma} (x-\mu)^2 \phi(x) dx + \int_{\mu-k\sigma}^{\mu+k\sigma} (x-\mu)^2 \phi(x) dx$$

$$+ \int_{\mu+k\sigma}^{\infty} (x-\mu)^2 \phi(x) dx.$$

Since $\phi(x) \geqslant 0$, being a probability function, the integrand $(x-\mu)^2 \phi(x) \geqslant 0$ and consequently the middle integral is non-negative. Hence we can say

$$\sigma^2 \geqslant \int_{-\infty}^{\mu-k\sigma} (x-\mu)^2 \phi(x)dx + \int_{\mu+k\sigma}^{\infty} (x-\mu)^2 \phi(x)dx.$$

For values of x in $(-\infty, \mu-k\sigma)$ it is clear that $(x-\mu)^2 \geqslant k^2\sigma^2$ and this result is also true for values of x in $(\mu+k\sigma, \infty)$.

Hence

$$\sigma^2 \geqslant k^2\sigma^2 \int_{-\infty}^{\mu-k\sigma} \phi(x)dx + k^2\sigma^2 \int_{\mu+k\sigma}^{\infty} \phi(x)dx.$$

$=$

$$\leqslant k^2\sigma^2 p(-\infty \leqslant x \leqslant \mu-k\sigma) + k^2\sigma^2 p(\mu+k\sigma \leqslant x \leqslant \infty).$$

Now $p(-\infty \leqslant x \leqslant \mu-k\sigma) + p(\mu+k\sigma \leqslant x \leqslant \infty) = p\{|x-\mu| > k\sigma\}$ and so finally, dividing throughout by $k^2\sigma^2$, the inequality is obtained.

§29. Convergence of relative frequency to probability.

By using the Chebyshev inequality we are now in a position to see more clearly what is meant by saying that relative frequency "converges" to probability. If the probability of an event E happening as the result of a trial of a system is p then we know that if n independent trials are made and if x denotes the total number of times E is found to occur in these trials then x is a discrete variate with the Bernoulli binomial distribution. In particular we know that the arithmetic mean of x is np and its standard deviation is $\sqrt{(npq)}$. The relative frequency of E is $z = x/n$ and it follows that z is a discrete variate (its possible values are $0, \frac{1}{n}, \frac{2}{n}, \ldots, \frac{n-1}{n}, 1$) with arithmetic mean $np/n = p$ and standard deviation $\sqrt{(npq)}/n = \sqrt{(pq/n)}$. Hence, by the Chebyshev inequality,

$$p\left\{|z-p| > k\sqrt{\left(\frac{pq}{n}\right)}\right\} \leqslant \frac{1}{k^2},$$

i.e., the probability that relative frequency calculated from n trials differs from the corresponding probability p by more than $k\sqrt{(pq/n)}$ is less than or equal to $1/k^2$.

For example if we take $k = 10$, $n = 10,000$, $p = q = \frac{1}{2}$ we see that the probability that the relative frequency z will not lie between $\frac{1}{2} \pm \frac{10}{200}$ is less than or equal to $\frac{1}{100}$.

Since $\sqrt{(pq/n)} \to 0$ as $n \to \infty$ the result which emerges is that for any preassigned $\varepsilon > 0$,

$$p\{|z-p| > \varepsilon\} \to 0 \quad \text{as } n \to \infty.$$

The relative frequency z is said to **converge in probability** or **converge stochastically** to the corresponding probability p in the sense that by taking a large enough number of trials the probability that z and p differ by any pre-assigned $\varepsilon > 0$ can be made negligibly small.

EXERCISES III

1. The probability density function of a continuous variate x is

$$\phi(x) = kx(1-x)e^x, \qquad 0 \leqslant x \leqslant 1.$$

Find the value of k and evaluate the arithmetic mean and the variance of the distribution.

2. A continuous variate x is distributed over the interval $[0, 1]$ with probability density function $ax^2 + bx$

where a, b are constants. If the arithmetic mean of x is 0·5, find the values of a and b.

3. Find the value of k such that

$$\phi(x) = \frac{k}{(1+x)^3}, \qquad 0 \leqslant x \leqslant \infty,$$

is a probability density function.

If five independent observations are made of x, what is the probability that exactly two of them will be greater than 1?

4. Obtain the arithmetic mean and the variance of the continuous variate x with probability density function

$$\phi(x) = \frac{1}{2^{\frac{1}{2}v}\,\Gamma(\frac{1}{2}v)} x^{\frac{1}{2}v-1} e^{-\frac{1}{2}x}, \qquad 0 \leqslant x \leqslant \infty.$$

5. If x is any variate prove that the expected value of $(x-c)^2$ is a minimum when $c = \mu$ where μ is the arithmetic mean of x.

6. A point P is chosen at random on a line XY of length $2c$. A second point Q is chosen on the larger of PX and PY. Find the probability that XQ is less than c.

7. Each of three hills is known to be independently any height between 1000 feet and 1500 feet, all heights within this interval being equally likely. What is the probability that the heights of no two of them differ by less than 100 feet?

8. If x and y are independent continuous variates with probability density functions

$$\phi(x) = e^{-x}, \qquad 0 \leqslant x \leqslant \infty; \quad \psi(y) = e^{-y}, \qquad 0 \leqslant y \leqslant \infty,$$

show that the probability density function for $z = x+y$ is given by

$$\Phi(z) = ze^{-z}, \qquad 0 \leqslant z \leqslant \infty.$$

9. If x and y are independent rectangular variates distributed in the interval $[0, 1]$, show that the probability density function for $z = x+y$ is

$$\Phi(z) = \begin{cases} z & 0 \leqslant z \leqslant 1 \\ 2-z & 1 \leqslant z \leqslant 2. \end{cases}$$

10. By observing that

$$\int_{-\infty}^{\infty} \frac{1}{\sqrt{(2\pi)}} e^{-\frac{1}{2}x^2} dx = 2\int_{0}^{\infty} \frac{1}{\sqrt{(2\pi)}} e^{-\frac{1}{2}x^2} dx,$$

using the change of variable $z = \frac{1}{2}x^2$, and the result that $\Gamma(\frac{1}{2}) = \sqrt{\pi}$, verify that

$$\int_{-\infty}^{\infty} \frac{1}{\sqrt{(2\pi)}} e^{-\frac{1}{2}x^2} dx = 1$$

and that the arithmetic mean and the variance of the standardised normal distribution are respectively 0 and 1.

Verify that the corresponding properties of the general normal distribution are μ and σ^2.

11. A variate has probability density function

$$\phi(x) = cf(x), \qquad x \geqslant k,$$

where k is a given number, c is a constant chosen to ensure that $\phi(x)$ is a probability density function and

$$f(x) = \frac{1}{\sqrt{(2\pi)}} e^{-\frac{1}{2}x^2}.$$

If $g(k) = \int_k^\infty f(x)\,dx$, show that the arithmetic mean and the variance of x are respectively

$$f(k)/g(k)$$

and

$$1 + \frac{f(k)}{g(k)}\left\{k - \frac{f(k)}{g(k)}\right\}.$$

12. Two independent events, A and B, must each happen once and only once in the future. The respective probability density functions of the times t_1 and t_2 which elapse before A and B happen are

$$k_1 a^{t_1},\ 0 \leqslant t_1 \leqslant \infty; \qquad k_2 b^{t_2},\ 0 \leqslant t_2 \leqslant \infty$$

where a and b are positive constants less than 1. Show that the probability that A happens before B is

$$\log_e a / (\log_e a + \log_e b).$$

13. The time taken to serve a customer is a continuous variate t, measured in hours, with probability density function

$$\phi(t) = 2t, \qquad 0 \leqslant t \leqslant 1.$$

If as soon as service is completed for the first customer a second customer is served and if the service times of successive customers are independent with probability function $\phi(t)$, what is the probability that service to both customers will be completed within one hour?

14. The time taken by A to solve a problem is a continuous variate t with probability density function

$$\phi(t) = e^{-t}, \qquad 0 \leqslant t \leqslant \infty.$$

The time taken by B to solve the problem is an independent continuous variate s with probability density function

$$\psi(s) = \tfrac{1}{2}e^{-s/2}, \quad 0 \leqslant s \leqslant \infty.$$

(i)   What is the probability that A solves the problem before B does?

(ii) What is the probability that the problem is solved within time T?

(iii) What is the probability that both solve the problem within time T and B does so before A?

15. The time taken by a mechanic to repair a machine is a continuous variate t with probability density function

$$\phi(t) = \lambda e^{-\lambda t}, \quad 0 \leqslant t \leqslant \infty.$$

(i) Find the probability that a repair will take longer than t_0 and find the average total time for a repair given that it has not been completed by time t_0.

(ii) A factory has three mechanics M_1, M_2, M_3 and the time taken by M_i, $i = 1, 2, 3$, to repair a machine is a continuous variate with probability density function $\phi_i(t) = \lambda_i e^{-\lambda_i t}$, $0 \leqslant t \leqslant \infty$. A machine to be repaired is assigned at random to one of the mechanics and at time t_0 the repair has not been completed. What is the probability that M_1 is doing the repair?

(iii) Given that a machine assigned at random to one of the three mechanics has not been repaired by time t_0, what is the expected or average additional time required to complete the job?

CHAPTER IV

OCCUPANCY, RUNS AND MATCHING

§30. Occupancy problems. When r distinguishable objects are placed at random independently and one at a time into a set of n distinguishable compartments, with no restriction on the number of objects placed in any compartment, there are n^r different possible equally likely distinguishable distributions of the objects, since each object can be placed in n different possible compartments.

If the r objects are indistinguishable it follows that the number of possible distinguishable distributions must be less than n^r since any interchange of positions of a pair of objects leaves the distribution unaltered. We now prove that this reduced number is $\binom{n+r-1}{r}$.

We can represent the situation diagrammatically by $n+1$ vertical lines denoting compartment boundaries and r letters "0" denoting the objects. For example when $n = 5$ and $r = 6$ a typical diagram of a possible distribution would be

$$| 00 | 0 | \quad | 000 | \quad |$$

corresponding to two objects in the first compartment, one in the second, none in the third, three in the fourth and none in the fifth.

Any distinguishable arrangement corresponds to one of the possible selections of r positions for the objects from the $n+1+r-2$, that is $n+r-1$, possible positions. The reduction by two in this number arises from the requirement that the two end positions in any proper diagram of objects and compartment boundaries must be taken by compartment boundaries represented by vertical lines. The number of such selections is $\binom{n+r-1}{r}$ and this proves the result.

This number $\binom{n+r-1}{r}$ is seen to be equal also to the number of distinguishable unordered sets of balls obtained by selecting r balls at random one at a time with replacement from a bag containing n distinguishable balls. The formula can alternatively be established by an enumerative argument and induction—see problem 3 on page 118.

Also of importance is the result that when $r \geqslant n$ the number of distinguishable distributions of r similar objects such that no compartment is empty is $\binom{r-1}{n-1}$. To prove this we must observe that the conditions now require that at most one bar can occur between any two letters "0". There are $n-1$ bars to be placed, excluding the two necessary end bars, and $r-1$ positions between letters for them, and so $\binom{r-1}{n-1}$ different possible selections of positions. Hence there must be $\binom{r-1}{n-1}$ distinguishable distributions of objects subject to the given restriction.

Example 4.1. If r similar six-sided dice are thrown, how many distinguishable joint results may appear?

Each die can show any one of six numbers without restriction. This means that each die can independently and without restriction be placed in any one of six different "compartments". Hence the number of distinguishable results must be $\binom{6+r-1}{r} = \binom{r+5}{r}$.

§31. Applications to statistical mechanics.

While it is usual to regard the n^r possible arrangements of r objects in n compartments, whether distinguishable or not, as equally likely and consequently as each having probability $1/n^r$, in theoretical physics it may be necessary to depart from such an assumption.

In the statistical mechanics treatment of the behaviour of r indistinguishable particles, all phase space is subdivided into a large number, n, of small cells and each particle is assigned to the cell which corresponds to its position and behaviour at the instant in question. Thus the state of the system of particles at any time is described by the corresponding distribution of the r particles over the n cells in phase space. When this distribution is completely random and independent all n^r cases are equally likely and the particles are described as behaving according to **Maxwell-Boltzmann statistics**. Modern theory has established that no known particles behave in this way, and that the proper description entails replacing the overall assumption of equal likelihood by one of two alternatives.

The behaviour of photons, nuclei and atoms containing an even number of elementary particles is suitably described by assuming that all distinguishable arrangements of particles are equally likely. As we have seen in §30 there are $\binom{n+r-1}{r}$ such distributions, and so each must have

probability $1\Big/\binom{n+r-1}{r}$. Particles behaving according to

this model are said to conform to **Bose-Einstein statistics**.

The behaviour of other known particles is described by assuming that no cell can contain more than one particle at any instant and that, subject to this restriction, all distinguishable arrangements are equally probable. From the restriction we must have $n \geqslant r$ and clearly the number of distinguishable arrangements is the number of selections of

r cells from n possible cells, that is $\binom{n}{r}$. Each arrangement

has thus probability $1\Big/\binom{n}{r}$ and particles of this type con-

form to **Fermi-Dirac statistics**.

Example 4.2. Find the probability that a specified cell contains exactly k particles when (i) Maxwell-Boltzmann and (ii) Bose-Einstein statistics describe the behaviour of the particles.

(i) The probability that a particle falls in the specified cell is $\frac{1}{n}$ and that it does not fall in that cell is $1-\frac{1}{n}=\frac{n-1}{n}$. In the Maxwell-Boltzmann model of independent random distribution, the number of particles falling in the specified cell must follow the Bernoulli binomial distribution for r trials with probability $\frac{1}{n}$ of success and $\frac{n-1}{n}$ of failure at any trial.

Required probability $= \binom{r}{k}\frac{1}{n^k}\left(\frac{n-1}{n}\right)^{r-k} = \binom{r}{k}\frac{(n-1)^{r-k}}{n^r}$.

(ii) Each distinguishable arrangement of particles has probability $\dfrac{1}{\dbinom{n+r-1}{r}}$. In enumerating favourable arrangements, there is no loss of generality in taking the first cell as the specified one. Then we see that for favourable arrangements three bars and k letters "0" are fixed thus:

$$k \text{ letters}$$
$$\big| \, 0\,0\ldots0 \, \big| \ldots\ldots\ldots\ldots\big|,$$

the last bar denoting the limit of the last remaining cells. Thus there is free arrangement possible of $r-k$ letters "0" and $n+1-3 = n-2$ bars and the number of distinguishable arrangements must be $\dbinom{n+r-k-2}{r-k}$.

Required probability $= \dbinom{n+r-k-2}{r-k} \div \dbinom{n+r-1}{r}$.

§32. Runs. In any ordered sequence of elements of two kinds, each maximal subsequence of elements of like kind is called a **run**. For example if the results of a sequence of Bernoulli trials were recorded we would have a sequence of the letters E and $\bar{E}$ denoting respectively the outcomes E and not-E. The first ten results might be $EEE\bar{E}EE\bar{E}\bar{E}EE$, and this would be described as starting with an E run of three followed by an $\bar{E}$ run of one, an E run of two, an $\bar{E}$ run of two and an E run of two. Obviously the E and $\bar{E}$ runs must alternate and so the total number of runs must always be one more than the number of pairs of unlike neighbours in the sequence.

If a sequence is formed by r_1 elements of one kind and r_2 elements of a second kind, all arrangements of these

$r_1 + r_2$ elements being equally likely, we now prove that the probability p_k of the sequence containing exactly k runs is given by

$$p_k = 2\binom{r_1-1}{v-1}\binom{r_2-1}{v-1}\bigg/\binom{r_1+r_2}{r_1} \quad \text{when } k = 2v,$$

$$p_k = \left\{\binom{r_1-1}{v}\binom{r_2-1}{v-1} + \binom{r_2-1}{v}\binom{r_1-1}{v-1}\right\}\bigg/\binom{r_1+r_2}{r_1}$$

when $k = 2v+1$.

There are $(r_1+r_2)!$ different possible equally likely permutations of the elements, but since any permutation among the r_1 first kind elements and among the r_2 second kind elements leaves the arrangement indistinguishable it follows that the $(r_1+r_2)!$ possible arrangements consist of $\dfrac{(r_1+r_2)!}{r_1!\,r_2!} = \binom{r_1+r_2}{r_1}$ distinguishable arrangements each consisting of $r_1!\,r_2!$ repetitions and hence being equally likely. Thus there are $\binom{r_1+r_2}{r_1}$ equally likely distinguishable arrangements of the elements, each having probability $1\bigg/\binom{r_1+r_2}{r_1}$.

When $k = 2v$, there must be v runs of each kind. The first run may be of either kind of element. The r_1 first kind elements may, by the result found in §30, be distributed in $\binom{r_1-1}{v-1}$ different ways into v compartments none of which is empty and similarly there are $\binom{r_2-1}{v-1}$ different distinguishable distributions of the r_2 second kind elements into exactly v runs. All the combinations of the kind of element in the first run, the distinguishable arrangements of r_1 and the distinguishable arrangements of r_2, are mutually exclusive, each with probability $1\Big/\binom{r_1+r_2}{r_1}$ and hence we have

$$p_k = 2\binom{r_1-1}{v-1}\binom{r_2-1}{v-1}\Big/\binom{r_1+r_2}{r_1} \quad \text{when } k = 2v.$$

When $k = 2v+1$, there are $v+1$ runs of the kind of element which forms the first run, and v runs of the other type of element and hence by similar reasoning we find

$$p_k = \left\{\binom{r_1-1}{v}\binom{r_2-1}{v-1}+\binom{r_2-1}{v}\binom{r_1-1}{v-1}\right\}\Big/\binom{r_1+r_2}{r_1}$$

when $k = 2v+1$.

§33. Success runs in Bernoulli trials. When a series of repeated independent Bernoulli trials is performed, with constant probability p of success at any trial, we can calculate the probability that there will be a run of exactly r consecutive successes in n trials. Provided $n/2 \leqslant r < n$ this is relatively straightforward. Then we know that there can be at most one such run. The probability of a run of exactly r consecutive successes commencing at the first trial is $p^r q$; the probability of such a run commencing at the second, third, fourth, ... or $(n-r)$th trials is in each case $p^r q^2$; the probability of such a run commencing at the $(n-r+1)$th trial is again $p^r q$. When $r \geqslant n/2$, these are all mutually exclusive events and thus the required probability must be given by

$$p\{\text{exactly } r \text{ successes in a run}\} = 2p^r q+(n-r-1)p^r q^2.$$

For $r = n$ the probability of a run of exactly r successes is simply p^n since all trials must be successes. Whenever

$r < n/2$, since the mutually exclusive description of the cases enumerated no longer holds, the evaluation of the required probability becomes rather complicated. We return to examine this case in §34.

It is of interest to observe that the expression $2p^r q + (n-r-1)p^r q^2$ always denotes the expected number of runs of exactly r consecutive successes in n trials for any $r < n$. This is true since the expected number of specified runs in n trials must be the total of the expected number of such runs which start at the first, second, third . . . and $(n-r+1)$th trials. In each case, there is either one or no such run and the probability of one such run is $p^r q$ for the first and the $(n-r+1)$th starting positions and $p^r q^2$ for all other starting positions.

Thus,

Expected number of runs of exact length r
$$= 1 \cdot p^r q + 1 \cdot p^r q^2 + 1 \cdot p^r q^2 + \ldots + 1 \cdot p^r q^2 + 1 \cdot p^r q$$
$$= 2p^r q + (n-r-1)p^r q^2.$$

The probability that a series of n trials should include a run of at least r consecutive successes is also readily obtained when $n/2 \leqslant r < n$. Now we see that the probability of such a run commencing at the first trial is p^r and at any trial from the second up to and including the $(n-r+1)$th is in each case qp^r. Since the restriction on r ensures that at most one such run can occur in n trials, the cases enumerated are once more mutually exclusive and so we have

$$p\{\text{run of at least } r \text{ consecutive successes}\} = p^r + (n-r)p^r q$$

for those values of r. For $r = n$ the required probability is obviously p^n.

For $r < n/2$ we find again that the mutually exclusive criterion no longer applies and the required probability becomes much more difficult to evaluate (see §34). By a similar argument to the one used above it can be verified that the expected number of success runs of length at least r is given by

$$p^r + (n-r)p^r q \text{ for all } 0 < r \leqslant n,$$

provided we interpret a run of $2r$ or more consecutive successes to be only one run of at least r consecutive successes.

Since a run of at least r consecutive successes must consist of a run of exactly r or exactly $(r+1)$ or exactly $(r+2) \ldots$ or exactly n consecutive successes, we ought to have for $n/2 \leqslant r < n$,

$$p\{\text{at least } r \text{ consecutive successes}\}$$

$$= \sum_{k=r}^{n} p\{\text{exactly } k \text{ consecutive successes}\}.$$

In fact we have

$$\text{R.H.S.} = \sum_{k=r}^{n-1} \{2p^k q + (n-k-1)p^k q^2\} + p^n$$

$$= 2p^r q \frac{1-p^{n-r}}{1-p} + (n-r-1)\frac{p^r q^2}{1-p} - \frac{q^2 p^{r+1}(1-p^{n-r-1})}{(1-p)^2} + p^n$$

$$= 2p^r - 2p^n + (n-r-1)p^r q - p^{r+1} + p^n + p^n$$

$$= (n-r)p^r q + 2p^r - qp^r - pp^r$$

$$= (n-r)p^r q + p^r$$

$$= \text{L.H.S.},$$

which verifies the relationship between our two formulae.

It should perhaps be emphasised that the expected number of runs in n trials is the average number of such runs we would obtain in many repetitions of a series of n trials, each such series being considered entirely separately and in no way as a continuation of a previous series of n trials.

§34. General treatment for runs of exact length r.

To examine the general probability for a run of exactly r consecutive successes appearing in a series of n Bernoulli trials and not subject to the restriction that $r \geqslant n/2$, it is best to use a recurrence relation technique. For convenience we examine the complementary probability and define v_n to be the probability that such a run does not occur in n trials. We observe that the absence of a run can occur in one of two mutually exclusive ways:

(i) the first $(n-1)$ trials contain no run of exactly r successes and such a run is not completed for the first time at the nth trial;

(ii) the first $(n-1)$ trials contain one run of exactly r successes which was completed at the $(n-1)$th trial and the nth trial was a success.

To find an expression for (i) we note that if there is no specified run in the first $(n-1)$ trials then either there is no such run in n trials or else there was no such run in $(n-r-1)$ trials followed by a failure, a run of $(r-1)$ consecutive successes at trials $(n-r+1)$, $(n-r+2)$, ..., $(n-1)$ and then a further success at the nth trial.

That is, probability of (i) $= v_{n-1} - v_{n-r-1}qp^r$.

The probability of (ii) is seen to be $v_{n-r-2}qp^rp$ or $v_{n-r-2}qp^{r+1}$, and so we have the equation for v_n:

$$v_n = v_{n-1} - qp^r v_{n-r-1} + qp^{r+1} v_{n-r-2}.$$

This recurrence relation, together with the initial conditions

$$v_0 = v_1 = v_2 = \ldots = v_{r-1} = 1,$$
$$v_r = 1 - p^r, \qquad v_{r+1} = 1 - 2qp^r$$

enables successive values of v_n and hence of $(1 - v_n)$ to be calculated.

Example 4.3. What is the probability that ten tosses of a symmetrical coin will contain at least one run of exactly four heads?

Let v_n denote the probability that n trials will contain no such run. We have

$$v_0 = v_1 = v_2 = v_3 = 1,$$
$$v_4 = 1 - (\tfrac{1}{2})^4 = \tfrac{15}{16},$$
$$v_5 = 1 - 2(\tfrac{1}{2})^4(\tfrac{1}{2}) = \tfrac{15}{16},$$

together with the relation

$$v_n = v_{n-1} - \tfrac{1}{32}v_{n-5} + \tfrac{1}{64}v_{n-6}.$$

Therefore

$$v_6 = v_5 - \tfrac{1}{32}v_1 + \tfrac{1}{64}v_0 = \tfrac{15}{16} - \tfrac{1}{32} + \tfrac{1}{64} = \tfrac{59}{64},$$
$$v_7 = v_6 - \tfrac{1}{32}v_2 + \tfrac{1}{64}v_1 = \tfrac{59}{64} - \tfrac{1}{32} + \tfrac{1}{64} = \tfrac{58}{64},$$
$$v_8 = v_7 - \tfrac{1}{32}v_3 + \tfrac{1}{64}v_2 = \tfrac{58}{64} - \tfrac{1}{32} + \tfrac{1}{64} = \tfrac{57}{64},$$
$$v_9 = v_8 - \tfrac{1}{32}v_4 + \tfrac{1}{64}v_3 = \tfrac{57}{64} - \tfrac{1}{32} \cdot \tfrac{15}{16} + \tfrac{1}{64} = \tfrac{449}{512},$$
$$v_{10} = v_9 - \tfrac{1}{32}v_5 + \tfrac{1}{64}v_4 = \tfrac{449}{512} - \tfrac{1}{32} \cdot \tfrac{15}{16} + \tfrac{1}{64} \cdot \tfrac{15}{16} = \tfrac{883}{1024}.$$

Required probability $= 1 - v_{10} = \tfrac{141}{1024}.$

It can be seen that while the method may be readily extended to deal with other values of n it becomes rather laborious when n is large.

§35. **General treatment for runs of length at least** r. A recurrence relation approach is again useful. Let u_n denote the probability that a series of n Bernoulli trials contains no run of at least r consecutive successes. We observe that if there is no run of length r in the first $(n-1)$ trials there will either be no such run in n trials or else the first run of r consecutive successes will be completed by a success at the nth trial. These two possibilities are mutually exclusive and cover all possible outcomes after the nth trial in those series of trials for which no run of length at least r had occurred after $(n-1)$ trials. The joint probability of the second alternative is $u_{n-r-1}qp^{r-1}p = qp^r u_{n-r-1}$. Thus we have the equation

$$u_{n-1} = u_n + qp^r u_{n-r-1},$$

which, with the particular values,

$$u_0 = u_1 = u_2 = \ldots = u_{r-1} = 1, \quad u_r = 1-p^r,$$

provides a method using successive substitution for obtaining u_n and consequently $(1-u_n)$ for any n.

If we write the recurrence relation in the form

$$u_{n-1} - u_n = qp^r u_{n-r-1}$$

and add together such equations for $n = r+1, r+2, \ldots, n$ we reach

$$u_r - u_n = qp^r \sum_{i=0}^{n-r-1} u_i \quad \text{for } n > r.$$

Now the left-hand side, being the difference between two probabilities, remains finite for all n and hence $\sum_{i=0}^{n-r-1} u_i$, being a series of positive terms, converges and consequently $u_n \to 0$ as $n \to \infty$.

Hence $u_r = qp^r \sum_{i=0}^{\infty} u_i$, and since $u_r = 1-p^r$ we have

$$\sum_{i=0}^{\infty} u_i = \frac{1-p^r}{qp^r}.$$

Now the probability that the first run of r successes is completed at the ith trial is $u_{i-1} - u_i$ and so, if we denote the expected or average number of trials required to complete the first run of r consecutive successes by e_r, we have

$$e_r = \sum_{i=1}^{\infty} (u_{i-1} - u_i)i$$

$$= \sum_{i=0}^{\infty} (i+1)u_i - \sum_{i=0}^{\infty} i\, u_i$$

$$= \sum_{i=0}^{\infty} u_i.$$

So we find that

$$e_r = \frac{1-p^r}{qp^r}.$$

It should be observed that, for general values of r and n, the probability of obtaining a run of exactly r successes is not always given by the probability of a run of at least r less the probability of a run of at least $(r+1)$. While this result is true when $r \geqslant n/2$, for general values of r and n it may be possible for a single series of n trials to contain both a run of exactly r successes and a run of at least $r+1$ successes. Obviously the probability of such a series contributes to the overall probability of obtaining a run of exactly r successes. However, since it also contributes to the overall probabilities of obtaining runs of at least r and of at least $(r+1)$ successes, its contribution is lost when the difference between these two probabilities is taken.

§36. **Runs of two kinds of elements.** It is possible to adopt a more detailed approach to the distribution of runs in a series of two kinds of element. Suppose we have a series of $A + B$ elements consisting of A elements of the first kind and B elements of the second kind and it is known that all permutations of these elements are equally likely. Let a_j denote the number of runs of first kind elements of length exactly j and b_j denote the number of runs of second kind elements of exact length j. Then, of course, we see that $\sum_{j=1}^{A} ja_j = A$, $\sum_{j=1}^{B} jb_j = B$. The total numbers of runs of first and second kind are given by $a = \sum_{j=1}^{A} a_j$ and $b = \sum_{j=1}^{B} b_j$ respectively and we again note that $|a - b|$ can only take the values 0 or 1.

For a specified set of values of a_j there are $a! \Big/ \prod_{j=1}^{A} a_j!$ different possible arrangements of elements of the first kind to form a runs, and similarly for a given set of values of b_j there are $b! \Big/ \prod_{j=1}^{B} b_j!$ different possible arrangements of elements of the second type to form b runs. When $|a - b| = 1$ that type of run of which there is the larger number must fill the first and every alternate position of the $a + b$ runs up to and including the last, so that no choice for the type of elements in the first run is available. When $a = b$, either type of run can commence the series, the remaining runs being alternately of the two types, i.e., there is a choice of two types of run for the first position.

If we define

$$\phi(a, b) = \begin{cases} 2 \text{ if } a = b \\ 1 \text{ if } |a - b| = 1, \\ 0 \text{ if } |a - b| > 1 \end{cases}$$

we find that the number of different arrangements of the $a_1, a_2, \ldots, a_A, b_1, b_2, \ldots, b_B$ runs must be

$$N(a, b) = \frac{a! \, b! \, \phi(a, b)}{\left\{\prod_{j=1}^{A} a_j!\right\} \left\{\prod_{j=1}^{B} b_j!\right\}}.$$

Now there are $\dfrac{(A+B)!}{A! \, B!}$ different possible arrangements of the $A + B$ elements and thus we have

$$p(a_j, j = 1, 2, \ldots, A; \, b_k, k = 1, 2, \ldots, B) =$$

$$\frac{a! \, b! \, \phi(a, b)}{\left\{\prod_{j=1}^{A} a_j!\right\} \left\{\prod_{j=1}^{B} b_j!\right\}} \bigg/ \frac{(A+B)!}{A! \, B!}.$$

By summing this joint probability over all the possible sets of values for the b_j, that is over all partitions of B such that $\sum_{j=1}^{B} b_j = b$ and $\sum_{j=1}^{B} jb_j = B$, we obtain the joint probability function for the a_j corresponding to a given value of b.

To obtain this, consider the identity

$$(t+t^2+t^3+ \ldots)^b = \frac{t^b}{(1-t)^b} = t^b \sum_{i=0}^{\infty} \frac{(b-1+i)!}{(b-1)! \, i!} t^i.$$

The coefficient of t^B on the L.H.S. is the sum of $b! \bigg/ \prod_{j=1}^{B} b_j!$ over all possible partitions of B such that $\sum_{j=1}^{B} jb_j = B$ and $\sum_{j=1}^{B} b_j = b$.

From the R.H.S. expansion this coefficient is

$$\frac{(b-1+B-b)!}{(b-1)!\,(B-b)!} = \frac{(B-1)!}{(b-1)!\,(B-b)!}$$

and hence the joint probability of the a_j and the given b is

$$p(a_j, j = 1, 2, \ldots, A; b) =$$

$$\frac{a!}{\prod\limits_{j=1}^{A} a_j!} \frac{(B-1)!\,\phi(a, b)}{(b-1)!\,(B-b)!} \Big/ \frac{(A+B)!}{A!\,B!}.$$

Now sum this with respect to the different possible values of b, and noting that the only values of b for which $\phi(a, b) \neq 0$ are $a-1$, a, $a+1$, we finally see that the joint probability function for the a_j is given by

$$p(a_j, j = 1, 2, \ldots, A) =$$

$$= \frac{a!}{\prod\limits_{j=1}^{A} a_j!} \left\{ \frac{(B-1)! \times 1}{(a-2)!(B-a+1)!} + \frac{(B-1)! \times 2}{(a-1)!(B-a)!} \right.$$

$$\left. + \frac{(B-1)! \times 1}{a!(B-a-1)!} \right\} \Big/ \frac{(A+B)!}{A!\,B!}$$

$$= \frac{a!}{\prod\limits_{j=1}^{A} a_j!} \frac{(B+1)!}{a!(B-a+1)!} \Big/ \frac{(A+B)!}{A!\,B!}$$

$$= \frac{(B+1)!}{\left\{ \prod\limits_{j=1}^{A} a_j! \right\}(B-a+1)!} \Big/ \frac{(A+B)!}{A!\,B!}.$$

A similar expression can be obtained showing the joint probability of the b_j.

By summing $p(a_j; b)$ over all the partitions of A satisfying $\sum_{j=1}^{A} a_j = a$ and $\sum_{j=1}^{A} ja_j = A$, we have the joint probability function for a and b given by

$$p(a, b) = \frac{(A-1)!\,(B-1)!\,\phi(a, b)}{(a-1)!\,(A-a)!\,(b-1)!\,(B-b)!} \bigg/ \frac{(A+B)!}{A!\,B!}.$$

Finally by summing $p(a, b)$ with respect to b we obtain

$$p(a) = \frac{(A-1)!\,(B+1)!}{(a-1)!\,(A-a)!\,a!\,(B-a+1)!} \bigg/ \frac{(A+B)!}{A!\,B!},$$

with a similarly obtainable expression for $p(b)$.

It is interesting to note that we can verify the result of §32 by summing $p(a, b)$ over those pairs of values for which $a+b = k$. When $k = 2v$, the only contribution comes from $p(v, v)$ which, since $\phi(v, v) = 2$, gives

$$p(\text{total of } 2v \text{ runs}) = 2\binom{A-1}{v-1}\binom{B-1}{v-1} \bigg/ \frac{(A+B)!}{A!\,B!}.$$

When $k = 2v+1$, we have to add $p(v, v+1)$ and $p(v+1, v)$ and in each case $\phi(a, b) = 1$ and so we again find that

$$p(\text{total of } 2v+1 \text{ runs}) =$$
$$\left\{ \binom{A-1}{v-1}\binom{B-1}{v} + \binom{A-1}{v}\binom{B-1}{v-1} \right\} \bigg/ \frac{(A+B)!}{A!\,B!}.$$

§37. Matching theory.

A problem which can be described in terms of two (or more) packs of cards is that of finding the probability of a specified number of matches. Suppose two packs of playing cards are separately thoroughly shuffled and then the top card is dealt from each pack. We say a **match** occurs if both cards are of the same suit. If the procedure is continued until all 52 pairs of cards are examined, we require to find the probability that exactly h matches occur, assuming that all possible permutations of the cards within each pack are equally likely. The problem may be extended to cover the probabilities of triple matches, or different types of double matches if three separate packs are used, but we shall confine our attention to the general problem with two packs of cards, both containing n cards.

Let pack A consist of n cards, each card belonging to one and only one of the k suits $C_1, C_2, \ldots, C_k$. Let $a_1, a_2, \ldots, a_k$ be the number of cards belonging to $C_1, C_2, \ldots, C_k$ respectively, $\sum_{i=1}^{k} a_i$ being equal to n. Let the second pack B also consist of n cards, the numbers of cards in the respective suits being b_i $(i = 1, 2, \ldots, k)$ where $\sum_{i=1}^{k} b_i = n$. The problem is to determine the probability of obtaining h matches under random pairing of the two packs, and since the number of different permutations of the two packs must be

$$N = \frac{n! \, n!}{\left\{\prod_{i=1}^{k} a_i!\right\} \left\{\prod_{i=1}^{k} b_i!\right\}}$$

it only remains to find the number of these permutations in which exactly h matches appear.

To do this, following Battin (1942), we introduce the enumerating function

$$\phi = \left\{ \sum_{i=1}^{k} \sum_{j=1}^{k} \alpha_i \beta_j e^{\delta_{ij}\theta} \right\}^n$$

where, as usual, $\delta_{ij} = 1$ when $i = j$ and $\delta_{ij} = 0$ when

It will be found that when $k = 2$ we have

$$p(h) = \frac{\binom{n}{h}\binom{h}{l}\binom{n-h}{m}}{\binom{n}{a_1}\binom{n}{b_2}}$$

where $l = \frac{1}{2}(a_1 - b_2 + h)$, $m = \frac{1}{2}(a_1 + b_2 - h)$, this expression for $p(h)$ applying only for values of h such that for the given a_1 and b_2 the values of $a_1 \pm (b_2 - h)$ are positive even integers or zero. For other values of h, we have $p(h) = 0$.

The results can be extended to cover two packs of cards consisting of unequal numbers of cards, n_1 and n_2 where say $n_1 > n_2$ by adding $n_1 - n_2$ dummy cards to the second pack and regarding them as a new suit. We would then have $k + 1$ suits with $a_{k+1} = 0$ and $b_{k+1} = n_1 - n_2$.

EXERCISES IV

1. A symmetrical tetrahedral die with faces numbered 1, 2, 3, 4 is thrown on to a table (i) five times; (ii) ten times; (iii) r times. At each throw the number on the face in contact with the table is noted. Find, in each case, the number of distinguishable joint results, ignoring order, which may appear and check the answers to (i) and (ii) by direct enumeration.

2. Ten cards are selected at random, one at a time with replacement from an ordinary pack of playing cards. Ignoring order and treating all cards as being distinguishable, how many distinguishable joint results can be obtained?

If all cards from the same suit are regarded as indistinguishable, how many unordered distinguishable joint results can appear?

3. If $K(n, r)$ denotes the number of distinguishable unordered sets of r balls that can be drawn at random—one ball at a time with replacement—from a bag containing n distinguishable balls, show that

$$K(n, r+1) = K(n, r)+K(n-1, r)+ \ldots +K(1, r).$$

Hence prove by induction that

$$K(n,r) = \binom{n+r}{n+1}-\binom{n+r-1}{n+1} = \binom{n+r-1}{r}.$$

4. One hundred particles are distributed over fifty cells. What is the probability that a specified cell contains exactly four particles when (i) the distribution is completely random; (ii) the distribution is such that all distinguishable arrangements of particles are equally likely?

5. The heights, in inches, of twelve plants growing in a row were found to be 24, 20, 27, 23, 29, 33, 36, 32, 24, 23, 30, 34.

Denote the six tallest plants by the letter T and the six smallest plants by the letter S and find the number of runs in the resulting pattern of twelve letters.

Calculate the probability that, if the arrangement of the letters was random, the number of runs would be equal to or less than that actually observed.

Hence examine whether there is evidence that tall plants tend to cluster together.

6. Find the probability of a run of (i) exactly three and (ii) at least three consecutive sixes if an unbiased die is thrown ten times.

What is the expected number of throws required to complete the first run of three consecutive sixes?

7. The expected number of runs of at least r consecutive successes in n repeated trials is

$$p^r + (n-r)p^r q.$$

Deduce the expected number of runs of at least r consecutive successes in $2n$ repeated trials and hence show that the difference between this and the total of the expected numbers of runs of at least r consecutive successes in two separate sets of n trials is

$$rp^r q - p^r.$$

Verify this result by direct evaluation of the net expected number of additional runs of at least r consecutive successes created when the two sets of n trials are regarded as one set of $2n$ consecutive trials.

8. Find the probability of twenty matches occurring under random pairing of two ordinary packs of playing cards,

   (i) if a match occurs whenever both cards are of the same colour;

  (ii) if a match occurs whenever both cards are honour cards (i.e., Ace, King, Queen, Jack, Ten) or both are not honour cards;

 (iii) if a match occurs whenever both cards are of the same suit.

CHAPTER V

RECURRENCE RELATIONS FOR PROBABILITIES

§38. Probabilities obtained directly from simple recurrence relations. In Chapter II we saw how certain probabilities could be obtained by first finding a recurrence relation, and then a generating function from the expansion of which an exact or asymptotic value for the required probability could be obtained. We now examine those problems which permit of a direct solution from the recurrence relation(s) without the intermediate step of introducing a generating function.

Suppose that two players A and B alternately throw a symmetrical cubical die, with faces 1, 2, 3, 4, 5, 6, and that the first player to throw a six wins. If A has first throw, what is the probability that he wins?

Let a be the probability that A wins. If A does not throw a six at his first throw, B will be in the same position as A was in originally and so will then have probability a of winning. Hence the probability that B wins, being the product of the probability that A does not throw a six at his first throw and the conditional probability that B then wins, is $\frac{5}{6}a$. The probability that the game is unfinished after n throws is $(\frac{5}{6})^n$ and since this tends to zero as $n \to \infty$ the sum of the probabilities of the game being won by A

or by B must be 1. Hence we have $a + \frac{5}{6}a = 1$, so that

$$a = \tfrac{6}{11}.$$

We could obtain this result by a different argument, which leads to a similar kind of equation. If A has probability a of winning, then if he throws a six on his first throw, the probability of this being $\frac{1}{6}$, he will win, or if he does not throw a six in his first throw and B also does not throw a six first time, A will have returned to the initial situation with conditional probability a of subsequently winning. Thus we must have

$$a = \tfrac{1}{6} + \tfrac{5}{6} \cdot \tfrac{5}{6}a,$$

which again gives the solution

$$a = \tfrac{6}{11}.$$

A more general form of the above problem is the following. Two players A and B play a game which consists of making alternate trials of two independent systems S_1 and S_2 having respective probabilities p_1 and p_2 of success and $q_1 = 1 - p_1$ and $q_2 = 1 - p_2$ of failure. A wins if the first success obtained is from the first system and we wish to find the probability of this result.

Let a be the probability that A wins. We observe that if the first trial of S_1 is a success, the game ends and A wins; if the first trial of S_1 is a failure and that of S_2 is a success, the game ends and B wins; if the first trials of both systems result in failures the game returns to its initial state. Thus we have the equation for a,

$$a = p_1 1 + q_1 p_2 0 + q_1 q_2 a,$$

whence

$$a = \frac{p_1}{1 - q_1 q_2}.$$

P I

Similarly, if b denotes the probability that B wins we find

$$b = \frac{q_1 p_2}{1 - q_1 q_2}$$

and we note that $a + b = 1$ showing that some one must emerge as winner.

If the rules are modified so that trials of S_1 and S_2 are made simultaneously and the simultaneous appearance of successes from both systems ends the game in a draw, the equation for a becomes

$$a = p_1 p_2 0 + p_1 q_2 1 + p_2 q_1 0 + q_1 q_2 a,$$

with the solution

$$a = \frac{p_1 q_2}{1 - q_1 q_2}.$$

Similarly

$$b = \frac{p_2 q_1}{1 - q_1 q_2}$$

and the probability that the game ends in a draw is given by $1 - a - b$.

§39. Probabilities obtained directly from simultaneous recurrence relations.

In a series of repeated independent Bernoulli trials what is the probability that a run of r consecutive successes will occur before the first run of s consecutive failures? To obtain this probability we must introduce two associated probabilities. Let α denote the conditional probability that the specified event E—a run of r successes before a run of s failures—happens when the first trial is known to have been a success, and let β denote the conditional probability of E when it is known that the first trial was a failure. Then, of course, the required probability is given by $p\alpha + q\beta$.

Now, when the first trial is a success, E can happen in the following mutually exclusive ways:

(i) the following $r-1$ trials are all successes, the probability of this being p^{r-1};

(ii) the first failure occurs at the kth trial where $2 \leqslant k \leqslant r$ and E subsequently happens. The conditional probability of first failure at kth trial is $p^{k-2}q$ and the conditional probability of the subsequent happening of E is, for any k, simply β.

From this we see that

$$\alpha = p^{r-1} + q\beta\{1 + p + p^2 + \ldots + p^{r-2}\} = p^{r-1} + \beta(1 - p^{r-1}).$$

Similarly, by considering the possible ways in which E can happen when the first trial is a failure, we find

$$\beta = p\alpha\{1 + q + q^2 + \ldots + q^{s-2}\} = \alpha(1 - q^{s-1}).$$

We now have two linear equations for α and β which have the solution

$$\alpha = \frac{p^{r-1}}{p^{r-1} + q^{s-1} - p^{r-1}q^{s-1}}, \quad \beta = \frac{p^{r-1}(1 - q^{s-1})}{p^{r-1} + q^{s-1} - p^{r-1}q^{s-1}},$$

whence the required probability is

$$p\alpha + q\beta = \frac{(1 - q^s)p^{r-1}}{p^{r-1} + q^{s-1} - p^{r-1}q^{s-1}}.$$

We can, by interchanging p with q and r with s, deduce from this that the probability of a run of s consecutive failures preceding the first run of r consecutive successes must be

$$\frac{q^{s-1}(1 - p^r)}{p^{r-1} + q^{s-1} - p^{r-1}q^{s-1}}$$

and we note that the sum of this and the above probability is unity.

A direct extension is the following problem. Repeated independent trials having three possible outcomes A, B and C, with respective probabilities p, q and r, where $p+q+r = 1$, are performed. What is the probability that a run of t consecutive As will occur before the first run of s consecutive Bs?

Let α denote the conditional probability that the specified event E happens if the first trial results in A;

β denote the conditional probability of E if the first trial results in B; and

γ denote the conditional probability of E if the first trial results in C.

Then the required probability is $p\alpha + q\beta + r\gamma$.

When the first trial gives A, the event E can happen in the following mutually exclusive ways:

(i) the following $t-1$ trials all give A, the probability of this being p^{t-1};

(ii) the following $k-2$ trials are A, the following trial results in B, and E then subsequently happens, for any k in the range $2 \leqslant k \leqslant t$, the probability of this being $p^{k-2}q\beta$;

(iii) the following $k-2$ trials are A, the following trial results in C, and E then subsequently happens for any k in the range $2 \leqslant k \leqslant t$, the probability of this being $p^{k-2}r\gamma$.

Thus we have

$$\alpha = p^{t-1} + q\beta(1 + p + p^2 + \ldots + p^{t-2}) + r\gamma(1 + p + p^2 + \ldots + p^{t-2}),$$

$$\alpha = p^{t-1} + \frac{(q\beta + r\gamma)}{1-p}(1 - p^{t-1}).$$

Similarly we can obtain the equations

$$\beta = \alpha p(1+q+q^2+ \ldots +q^{s-2})+\gamma r(1+q+q^2+ \ldots +q^{s-2}),$$
$$\beta = \frac{(\alpha p+\gamma r)(1-q^{s-1})}{(1-q)},$$

and

$$\gamma = \alpha p(1+r+r^2+ \ldots)+\beta q(1+r+r^2+ \ldots),$$
$$\gamma = \frac{(\alpha p+\beta q)}{(1-r)}.$$

From the final equation we notice that $\gamma = \alpha p + \beta q + r\gamma$ which is the required probability and thus we must simply eliminate α and β from the three equations which we have obtained. Finally we have

Required probability =

$$\frac{p^t(1-p)(1-q^s)}{(1-p)p^t+(1-q)q^s-(2-p-q)p^t q^s}.$$

§40. Linear difference equations with constant coefficients.
In certain problems probabilities can be found by forming a recurrence relation and using the theory of difference equations to provide a direct solution to the recurrence relation.

We introduce the operator E from unit-interval finite difference calculus defined by

$$Eu_n = u_{n+1}$$
$$E^2u_n = EEu_n = Eu_{n+1} = u_{n+2}$$
$$\ldots \ldots \ldots \ldots \ldots \ldots \ldots$$
$$E^ru_n = u_{n+r}.$$

The general linear difference equation of order r with constant coefficients is

$$\phi(E)u_n = f(n),$$

where $\phi(E)$ is a polynomial of degree r in E and where, for simplicity, we may assume that the coefficient of E^r is 1.

First we consider the special class of such equations for which $f(n) \equiv 0$, that is equations of the form

$$\phi(E)u_n = 0.$$

When $\phi(E) \equiv (E-\lambda_1)(E-\lambda_2)\ldots(E-\lambda_r)$ where λ_i are constants which are all distinct from one another, it can be shown that the most general solution of the equation $\phi(E)u_n = 0$ is

$$u_n = a_1\lambda_1^n + a_2\lambda_2^n + \ldots + a_r\lambda_r^n,$$

where $a_1, a_2, \ldots, a_r$ are arbitrary constants.

When $\phi(E)$ contains a repeated factor $(E-\lambda_\alpha)^h$ the corresponding part of the general solution becomes

$$\lambda_\alpha^n(a_\alpha + a_{\alpha+1}n + a_{\alpha+2}n^{(2)} + \ldots + a_{\alpha+h-1}n^{(h-1)})$$

where $n^{(k)}$ is the kth factorial power of n defined by

$$n^{(k)} = n(n-1)(n-2)\ldots(n-k+1).$$

Example 5.1. Solve $u_{n+3} - u_{n+2} - 14u_{n+1} + 24u_n = 0$.

The equation may be written in the form.

$$(E^3 - E^2 - 14E + 24)u_n = 0,$$
$$(E-2)(E-3)(E+4)u_n = 0.$$

The general solution is therefore

$$u_n = a \cdot 2^n + b \cdot 3^n + c \cdot (-4)^n \text{ where } a, b, c \text{ are constants.}$$

Example 5.2. Find the general solution of the equation

$$u_{n+4} - 9u_{n+3} + 30u_{n+2} - 44u_{n+1} + 24u_n = 0$$

and hence obtain the particular solution which satisfies the conditions

$$u_0 = 1, \quad u_1 = 5, \quad u_2 = 1, \quad u_3 = -45.$$

The equation may be written in the form

$$(E^4 - 9E^3 + 30E^2 - 44E + 24)u_n = 0,$$
$$(E-2)^3(E-3)u_n = 0.$$

The general solution is therefore

$$u_n = 2^n(a + bn + cn(n-1)) + d \cdot 3^n$$

where a, b, c, d are constants.

For the particular solution we have

$$u_0 = a + d = 1,$$
$$u_1 = 2a + 2b + 3d = 5,$$
$$u_2 = 4a + 8b + 8c + 9d = 1,$$
$$u_3 = 8a + 24b + 48c + 27d = -45,$$

whence $a = 0, \quad b = 1, \quad c = -2, \quad d = 1.$

The particular solution is therefore

$$u_n = 2^n(n - 2n(n-1)) + 3^n,$$
$$= 2^n n(3 - 2n) + 3^n.$$

The solution of linear difference equations when $f(n) \not\equiv 0$ is analogous to that of linear differential equations with constant coefficients. The general solution is first found for the equation

$$\phi(E)u_n = 0,$$

and a particular solution is found for the equation

$$\phi(E)u_n = f(n).$$

The general solution of this latter equation is then given by the sum of its particular solution and the general solution of the former equation. Thus to solve these more general equations, the only additional problem which arises is the identification of particular solutions of the equations. It is not proposed to give a general treatment of this problem, but merely to examine the particular solution for several common forms of $f(n)$.

(i) When $f(n) = k\mu^n$, where k is a given constant, and $\mu \neq \lambda_i$ for $i = 1, 2, \ldots, r$, then it can be verified that $\dfrac{k\mu^n}{\phi(\mu)}$ is a particular solution of the equation $\phi(E)u_n = k\mu^n$.

Example 5.3. The general solution of $u_{n+2} - 5u_{n+1} + 6u_n = 3(4^n)$ is $u_n = a \cdot 2^n + b \cdot 3^n + \frac{3}{2} \cdot 4^n$ where a, b are arbitrary constants.

(ii) When $f(n) = k\mu^n$, where k is a given constant, and $\mu = \lambda_i$ where $(E - \lambda_i)$ is a non-repeated factor of $\phi(E)$, then $\dfrac{kn\mu^{n-1}}{\phi'(\mu)}$ is a particular solution of the equation $\phi(E)u_n = k\mu^n$, where $\phi'(\mu)$ denotes $\left(\dfrac{d}{dE}\phi(E)\right)_{E=\mu}$.

Example 5.4. The general solution of $u_{n+2} - 5u_{n+1} + 6u_n = 3(2^n)$ is $u_n = a \cdot 2^n + b \cdot 3^n + \dfrac{3 \cdot n \cdot 2^{n-1}}{-1}$

$$= \left(a - \frac{3n}{2}\right)2^n + b \cdot 3^n \text{ where } a, b \text{ are arbitrary constants.}$$

(iii) When $f(n) = k\mu^n$, where k is a given constant, and $\mu = \lambda_i$ where $(E-\lambda_i)$ is a factor of $\phi(E)$ which is repeated r times, then

$$\frac{kn(n-1)\dots(n-r+1)\mu^{n-r}}{\phi^{(r)}(\mu)}$$

is a particular solution of the equation $\phi(E)u_n = k\mu^n$,

where
$$\phi^{(r)}(\mu) = \left(\frac{d^r}{dE^r}\phi(E)\right)_{E=\mu}.$$

Example 5.5. The general solution of the equation

$$(E-2)^3(E-3)u_n = 5 \cdot 2^n$$

is $\quad u_n = \{a+bn+cn(n-1)\}2^n + d \cdot 3^n + \dfrac{5n(n-1)(n-2)2^{n-3}}{-6}$

where a, b, c, d are arbitrary constants.

(iv) When $f(n)$ is a polynomial in n, it is necessary to re-express it in the form of a factorial polynomial by elementary algebra so that we have

$$f(n) = a_0 + a_1 n + a_2 n^{(2)} + \dots.$$

To find the particular solution we must introduce the difference operator Δ defined by $\Delta u_n = u_{n+1} - u_n = (E-1)u_n$. From the symbolic relationship $E = 1+\Delta$ we can express $\phi(E)$ as $\psi(\Delta)$ and the particular solution is obtained from

$$u_n = \frac{1}{\phi(E)} f(n) = \frac{1}{\psi(\Delta)} f(n),$$

by expanding $\dfrac{1}{\psi(\Delta)}$ in powers of Δ and using the easily established results

$$\Delta n^{(r)} = r n^{(r-1)},$$

$$\Delta^2 n^{(r)} = r(r-1) n^{(r-2)},$$

$$\cdots,$$

$$\Delta^k n^{(r)} = r(r-1) \ldots (r-k+1) n^{(r-k)} \text{ for } k \leqslant r,$$

$$\Delta^k n^{(r)} = 0 \text{ for } k > r,$$

and

$$\Delta^{-1} n^{(r)} = \frac{n^{(r+1)}}{r+1},$$

$$\Delta^{-2} n^{(r)} = \frac{n^{(r+2)}}{(r+1)(r+2)},$$

$$\cdots,$$

$$\Delta^{-k} n^{(r)} = \frac{n^{(r+k)}}{(r+1)(r+2) \ldots (r+k)}.$$

Example 5.6. Find a particular solution of the equation

$$u_{n+2} - 7u_{n+1} + 12u_n = 3n^2 + 2n + 2.$$

First we have $3n^2 + 2n + 2 = 3n^{(2)} + 5n^{(1)} + 2$ and so the required solution is obtained from

$$u_n = \frac{1}{E^2 - 7E + 12} (3n^2 + 2n + 2)$$

$$= \frac{1}{(2-\Delta)(3-\Delta)} (3n^{(2)} + 5n^{(1)} + 2).$$

That is

$$u_n = \frac{1}{6}\left(1-\frac{\Delta}{2}\right)^{-1}\left(1-\frac{\Delta}{3}\right)^{-1}(3n^{(2)}+5n^{(1)}+2)$$

$$= \frac{1}{6}\left(1+\frac{\Delta}{2}+\frac{\Delta^2}{4}+\ldots\right)\left(1+\frac{\Delta}{3}+\frac{\Delta^2}{9}+\ldots\right)$$
$$(3n^{(2)}+5n^{(1)}+2)$$

$$= \frac{1}{6}(1+\frac{5}{6}\Delta+\frac{19}{36}\Delta^2+\ldots)(3n^{(2)}+5n^{(1)}+2)$$

$$= \frac{1}{2}n^{(2)}+\frac{5}{6}n^{(1)}+\frac{1}{3}+\frac{5}{6}n^{(1)}+\frac{25}{36}+\frac{19}{36}$$

$$= \frac{1}{2}n^2-\frac{1}{2}n+\frac{5}{6}n+\frac{5}{6}n+\frac{56}{36}$$

$$= \frac{1}{2}n^2+\frac{7}{6}n+\frac{14}{9}.$$

Example 5.7. Find a particular solution of the equation

$$u_{n+3}-5u_{n+2}+7u_{n+1}-3u_n = n^2+4n+1.$$

As previously, the required solution is given by

$$u_n = \frac{1}{\Delta^2(\Delta-2)}\{n^{(2)}+5n^{(1)}+1\}$$

$$= -\frac{1}{2}\Delta^{-2}\left\{1+\frac{\Delta}{2}+\frac{\Delta^2}{4}+\frac{\Delta^3}{8}+\frac{\Delta^4}{16}+\ldots\right\}(n^{(2)}+5n^{(1)}+1)$$

$$= -\frac{1}{2}(\Delta^{-2}+\frac{1}{2}\Delta^{-1}+\frac{1}{4}+\frac{1}{8}\Delta+\frac{1}{16}\Delta^2+\ldots)(n^{(2)}+5n^{(1)}+1)$$

$$= -\frac{1}{2}\left(\frac{n^{(4)}}{4.3}+\frac{n^{(3)}}{2.3}+\frac{1}{4}n^{(2)}+\frac{2}{8}n^{(1)}+\frac{2}{16}\right.$$

$$\left.+\frac{5n^{(3)}}{3.2}+\frac{5n^{(2)}}{2.2}+\frac{5}{4}n^{(1)}+\frac{5}{8}+\frac{n^{(2)}}{2.1}+\frac{1}{2}n^{(1)}+\frac{1}{4}\right)$$

$$= -\frac{1}{2}(\frac{1}{12}n^4+\frac{1}{2}n^3-\frac{1}{12}n^2+\frac{3}{2}n+1).$$

§41. Probabilities obtained by solving linear difference equations.

One of the classical problems in probability is that known as the "gambler's ruin problem". Two players

A and B play a series of independent games in which the probability of winning a single game is p for A and $q = 1 - p$ for B. After each game the loser pays £1 to the winner, and the series of games continues until one player has lost all his money. If initially A has £a and B has £b, what is the probability that A wins the series?

Since the enumeration of the different possible sets of results which would make A the ultimate winner would prove to be complicated, the recurrence relation technique is adopted.

Let u_{n+1} be the conditional probability that A will win the series if he has reached the stage of having £$(n+1)$.

The next game has two possible results:

either A wins—the probability of this being p—and then has £$(n+2)$,

or B wins—the probability of this being q—and A then has £n.

Since these cover all possible outcomes, it follows that

$$u_{n+1} = pu_{n+2} + qu_n, \quad 0 < n+1 < a+b.$$

Hence

$$pu_{n+2} - u_{n+1} + qu_n = 0.$$

In general $p \neq q$, and we shall first solve the problem on this assumption. Here we have, in the notation of § 40,

$$(pE^2 - E + q)u_n = 0,$$
$$(pE - q)\,(E - 1)u_n = 0,$$
$$(E - q/p)\,(E - 1)u_n = 0.$$

Thus $u_n = c_1\left(\dfrac{q}{p}\right)^n + c_2(1)^n$ where c_1 and c_2 are constants to be determined from the given conditions of the problem.

When $n = a+b$, A has $£(a+b)$ and so A must have won the series, i.e., $u_{a+b} = 1$. When $n = 0$, A has lost the series, i.e., $u_0 = 0$.

Substituting we have

$$c_1\left(\frac{q}{p}\right)^{a+b} + c_2 = 1,$$

$$c_1 + c_2 = 0,$$

whence $c_1 = \dfrac{p^{a+b}}{q^{a+b} - p^{a+b}}$ and $c_2 = \dfrac{-p^{a+b}}{q^{a+b} - p^{a+b}}$; hence

$$u_n = \frac{p^{a+b}\left(\dfrac{q}{p}\right)^n - p^{a+b}}{q^{a+b} - p^{a+b}}.$$

Now, initially A has $£a$ and so, at the start of the series of games, the probability that A wins is u_a.

Required probability $= u_a = \dfrac{p^b(q^a - p^a)}{q^{a+b} - p^{a+b}}$.

In the particular case when $p = q = \frac{1}{2}$, the general solution of the linear difference equation is found to be

$$u_n = c_1 + c_2 n.$$

Using the conditions $u_{a+b} = 1$ and $u_0 = 0$ we find that

$$u_n = \frac{n}{a+b}$$

and so the initial probability that A wins the series is

$$u_a = \frac{a}{a+b}.$$

Another form of the same problem is the following one-dimensional random walk of a particle. The particle, starting from the origin, makes a series of independent moves of unit distance along the x-axis with, at each stage, a probability p of moving to the right and q of moving to the left, until it first reaches $x = -a$ or $x = b$. The probability that it ends at $x = b$, not having previously passed through $x = -a$, is u_a of the gambler's ruin problem.

Example 5.8. A square board is divided into 16 equal squares by lines drawn parallel to its sides and a counter is initially placed at random on one of these squares. The counter is then moved n times. At each move, it is transferred to a neighbouring square in any direction horizontally, vertically or diagonally, all such transfers being equally likely. Find, for each of the 16 squares of the board, the probability that it is occupied after n such independent moves.

C	S	S	C
S	M	M	S
S	M	M	S
C	S	S	C

From symmetry it follows that the 16 squares may be classified into three types which we may refer to as C (corner), S (side) and M (middle). The problem is to find the respective probabilities of any specified C, S, or M being occupied after n moves, since all C squares will have equal probabilities, all S squares equal probabilities and all M squares equal probabilities.

Let c_n, s_n, m_n denote the respective probabilities that after n moves a specific C, S or M is occupied. From the diagram we note that from a C square the counter is equally likely to move to any of the three neighbouring squares, two of which are S and one M. Similarly, from an S square there are five equally likely moves, two to S, two to M and one to C; and from an M there are eight equally likely moves, four to S, three to M and one to C. By considering the different possible positions of the counter after n and $(n-1)$ moves we can obtain for $n \geqslant 1$,

$$c_n = \tfrac{2}{5}s_{n-1} + \tfrac{1}{8}m_{n-1}, \tag{1}$$

$$s_n = \tfrac{1}{3}c_{n-1} + \tfrac{2}{8}m_{n-1} + \tfrac{2}{5}s_{n-1}, \tag{2}$$

$$m_n = \tfrac{1}{3}c_{n-1} + \tfrac{3}{8}m_{n-1} + \tfrac{4}{5}s_{n-1}, \tag{3}$$

together with the obvious equation

$$4c_n + 8s_n + 4m_n = 1, \tag{4}$$

since the counter must be in some square after n moves.

Subtracting (2) from (3), we obtain

$$m_n - s_n = \tfrac{1}{8}m_{n-1} + \tfrac{2}{5}s_{n-1}.$$

Thus, from (1),

$$m_n = s_n + c_n.$$

Using this and (4) it follows that

$$c_n = \tfrac{1}{8} - \tfrac{3}{2}s_n,$$
$$m_n = \tfrac{1}{8} - \tfrac{1}{2}s_n,$$

and substituting these values in (1) we obtain

$$\tfrac{1}{8} - \tfrac{3}{2}s_n = \tfrac{2}{5}s_{n-1} + \tfrac{1}{8}(\tfrac{1}{8} - \tfrac{1}{2}s_{n-1}),$$
$$\tfrac{3}{2}s_n + \tfrac{27}{80}s_{n-1} = \tfrac{7}{64},$$
$$s_{n+1} + \tfrac{9}{40}s_n = \tfrac{7}{96},$$
$$(E + \tfrac{9}{40})s_n = \tfrac{7}{96} \cdot 1^n,$$

Thus

$$s_n = A(-\tfrac{9}{40})^n + \frac{\tfrac{7}{96}}{1 + \tfrac{9}{40}}$$

$$= \tfrac{5}{84} + A(-\tfrac{9}{40})^n,$$

whence

$$m_n = \tfrac{8}{84} - \tfrac{1}{2}A(-\tfrac{9}{40})^n,$$

and

$$c_n = \tfrac{3}{84} - \tfrac{3}{2}A(-\tfrac{9}{40})^n, \text{ for } n \geqslant 1.$$

To find A, we note that $s_0 = m_0 = c_0 = \tfrac{1}{16}$, since initial placing is random, and by substitution in (1) for $n = 1$ we find

$$c_1 = \tfrac{2}{5} \cdot \tfrac{1}{16} + \tfrac{1}{8} \cdot \tfrac{1}{16} = \tfrac{21}{640}.$$

Hence

$$\tfrac{3}{84} - \tfrac{3}{2}A(-\tfrac{9}{40}) = \tfrac{21}{640},$$

so that

$$A = \tfrac{-13}{1512},$$

which completes the solution.

It is interesting to notice that as $n \to \infty$, $s_n \to \tfrac{5}{84}$, $m_n \to \tfrac{8}{84}$ and $c_n \to \tfrac{3}{84}$ and that the ratios of these three probabilities are the same as the ratios between the numbers of squares adjacent to S, M and C squares.

Example 5.9. Of three bags, the first contains a proportion α of red balls and $(1-\alpha)$ of yellow balls, the second a proportion β of yellow balls and $(1-\beta)$ of green balls, and the third a proportion γ of green balls and $(1-\gamma)$ of red balls where $0 < \alpha,\ \beta,\ \gamma < 1$. A ball is drawn from the first bag and then replaced. If it is red, a ball is then drawn from the second bag and replaced, but if it is yellow, a ball is drawn from the third bag and replaced. This process continues, a ball being drawn from the first, second or third bag according as the previous ball drawn was green, red or yellow. Find the respective probabilities of the nth ball drawn being red, yellow or green, and show that these probabilities tend to limits as $n \to \infty$.

Let $r_n,\ y_n$ and g_n denote the probabilities that the nth ball drawn is red, yellow or green.

Then the following relations must be satisfied for $n \geqslant 2$:

$$r_n = (1-\gamma)y_{n-1} + \alpha g_{n-1}, \tag{1}$$

$$y_n = \beta r_{n-1} + (1-\alpha)g_{n-1}, \tag{2}$$

$$g_n = (1-\beta)r_{n-1} + \gamma y_{n-1}, \tag{3}$$

$$r_n + y_n + g_n = r_{n-1} + y_{n-1} + g_{n-1} = 1. \tag{4}$$

Substituting in (1) from (4) we obtain

$$r_n = (1-\gamma)(1 - r_{n-1} - g_{n-1}) + \alpha g_{n-1},$$

so that

$$g_{n-1} = \frac{(1-\gamma) - r_n - (1-\gamma)r_{n-1}}{1 - \alpha - \gamma}. \tag{5}$$

Substituting in (2) from (4) we obtain

$$1 - r_n - g_n = \beta r_{n-1} + (1-\alpha)g_{n-1},$$

and using (5) to express g_{n-1} and g_n in terms of $r_{n-1},\ r_n,\ r_{n+1}$ we find

$$r_{n+1} + r_n + (1 - \alpha - \beta - \gamma + \alpha\beta + \alpha\gamma + \beta\gamma)r_{n-1} = 1 - \gamma + \alpha\gamma,$$

which gives

$$\{E^2 + E + (1 - \alpha - \beta - \gamma + \alpha\beta + \alpha\gamma + \beta\gamma)\}r_n = 1 - \gamma + \alpha\gamma.$$

Hence, solving this difference equation, we have

$$r_n = \frac{1 - \gamma + \alpha\gamma}{3 - \alpha - \beta - \gamma + \alpha\beta + \alpha\gamma + \beta\gamma} + A(\lambda_1)^n + B(\lambda_2)^n,$$

where the values of λ_1 and λ_2 are

$$\tfrac{1}{2}[-1 \pm \sqrt{\{1 - 4(1 - \alpha - \beta - \gamma + \alpha\beta + \alpha\gamma + \beta\gamma)\}}].$$

Now

$$4(1 - \alpha - \beta - \gamma + \alpha\beta + \alpha\gamma + \beta\gamma) =$$
$$4\{(1 - \alpha)\,(1 - \beta)\,(1 - \gamma) + \alpha\beta\gamma\} > 0,$$

and

$$4(1 - \alpha - \beta - \gamma + \alpha\beta + \alpha\gamma + \beta\gamma) <$$
$$4(1 - \alpha + \alpha)\,(1 - \beta + \beta)\,(1 - \gamma + \gamma) = 4,$$

and so it follows that $|\lambda_1|$ and $|\lambda_2|$ are both less than 1. Therefore as $n \to \infty$, $\lambda_1^n \to 0$ and $\lambda_2^n \to 0$, so that

$$r_n \to r = \frac{1 - \gamma + \alpha\gamma}{3 - \alpha - \beta - \gamma + \alpha\beta + \alpha\gamma + \beta\gamma}.$$

Similarly

$$y_n \to y = \frac{1 - \alpha + \alpha\beta}{3 - \alpha - \beta - \gamma + \alpha\beta + \alpha\gamma + \beta\gamma},$$

and

$$g_n \to g = \frac{1 - \beta + \gamma\beta}{3 - \alpha - \beta - \gamma + \alpha\beta + \alpha\gamma + \beta\gamma}.$$

To obtain the values of A and B which give the full solution for r_n for finite n it is only necessary to substitute known values for r_2 and r_3. Similarly, general solutions could be obtained for y_n and g_n.

It is instructive to observe that if r_n, y_n and g_n tend respectively to r, y and g as $n \to \infty$, then so do r_{n-1}, y_{n-1} and g_{n-1}, and so, if these limits exist, they must satisfy the equations

$$r - (1-\gamma)y - \alpha g = 0,$$
$$-\beta r + y - (1-\alpha)g = 0,$$
$$-(1-\beta)r - \gamma y + g = 0,$$
$$r + y + g = 1.$$

Only three of these equations are linearly independent, and their unique solutions agree with the values obtained above for the limits of r_n, y_n and g_n.

§42. Expected durations by linear difference equations.

A second feature of interest in the gambler's ruin or one-dimensional random walk problem is the expected number of games or moves needed to reach a decision. In the first case, games continue until one player loses all his money; in the second case, the particle continues to make unit moves until it reaches $x = -a$ or $x = b$. The difference equation again provides a convenient method for solving this problem.

If e_n denotes the expected number of further games (or moves) needed to reach a decision after the stage at which player A has £n (in the random walk problem this corresponds to the particle being at $x = n-a$) then it follows that

$$e_n = 1 + pe_{n+1} + qe_{n-1}, \qquad 0 < n < a+b.$$

This expression is obtained by observing that one further

game or move must occur (except in the special cases $n = 0$ or $a+b$) which will, with probability p, take the system to "state" $n+1$ when there will be e_{n+1} expected subsequent games or moves or, with probability q, to "state" $n-1$ when there will be e_{n-1} expected subsequent games or moves. Thus, by the definition of expected values, the above equation must be true.

The expected duration e_n must therefore satisfy the difference equation

$$(pE^2 - E + q)e_n = -1$$

subject to the boundary conditions $e_0 = 0$ and $e_{a+b} = 0$.

Provided $p \neq q$, the general solution of $(pE^2 - E + q)e_n = 0$ is $e_n = c_1\left(\dfrac{q}{p}\right)^n + c_2(1)^n$. From §40 we find that a particular solution of

$$(pE^2 - E + q)e_n = -1 \cdot 1^n$$

is

$$e_n = \frac{-1 \cdot n \cdot 1^{n-1}}{2p-1} = \frac{-n}{p-q},$$

and so the general solution for e_n is

$$e_n = c_1\left(\frac{q}{p}\right)^n + c_2(1)^n - \frac{n}{p-q}.$$

Substituting the boundary conditions to determine c_1 and c_2 we have

$$0 = c_1 + c_2,$$
$$0 = c_1\left(\frac{q}{p}\right)^{a+b} + c_2 - \frac{a+b}{p-q},$$

whence

$$c_1 = -c_2 = \frac{p^{a+b}(a+b)}{(q^{a+b}-p^{a+b})(p-q)}.$$

Thus the expected number of games to be played, or moves of the particle to be made, before one or other of the final results is reached is

$$e_a = \frac{a}{q-p} + \frac{a+b}{p-q}\left\{\frac{q^a-p^a}{q^{a+b}-p^{a+b}}\right\}p^b$$

$$= \frac{aq^{a+b}+bp^{a+b}-(a+b)q^ap^b}{(q-p)(q^{a+b}-p^{a+b})}.$$

In the special case when $p = q = \frac{1}{2}$, the difference equation for e_n becomes

$$(E-1)^2 e_n = -2,$$

and the general solution of this equation is found to be

$$e_n = c_1 + c_2 n - n^2.$$

Since $e_0 = 0$, it follows that $c_1 = 0$, and from $e_{a+b} = 0$ we have

$$c_2(a+b)-(a+b)^2 = 0.$$

Therefore

$$c_1 = 0, \quad c_2 = (a+b),$$

and so

$$e_n = (a+b)n - n^2.$$

Thus the initial expected duration must be

$$e_a = (a+b)a - a^2 = ab.$$

EXERCISES V

1. Three players A, B, C play under the following conditions. In each game the probability of success is the same for each of the two contestants. A and B play together in the first game, the winner next playing a game against C and if he also wins this game he wins the series; if he loses to C then C next plays against the third player and so on until one player wins two successive games.

If p denotes the conditional probability that A wins the series when he is in the position of having won the game which has just been played but not also the one preceding it, show that

$$p = \tfrac{1}{2} + \tfrac{1}{8}p,$$

and that the initial probability that A wins the series is

$$\tfrac{1}{2}p + \tfrac{1}{8}p.$$

Hence find the probability that C wins the series.

2. The probability of survival for five years at certain ages is given in the following table.

Age	70	75	80	85
Survival probability	p	$\tfrac{3}{4}p$	$\tfrac{2}{3}p$	$\tfrac{1}{2}p$

Four men are aged 70, 75, 80, 85 respectively. Find the probabilities that (i) all will live to age 90; (ii) none will live to age 90; (iii) exactly one will die before the age of 85.

If $p = \tfrac{4}{5}$, what is the probability that the man aged 70 will live to a greater age than the man aged 85?

3. A series of independent games is played by A and B whose respective probabilities of winning any single game are p and $1 - p$. If the series is won by the first player to

establish a lead of two games, show that if π denotes the probability that A wins the series then

$$\pi = p^2 + 2p(1-p)\pi.$$

Alternatively the series is won by a player after five games if he then leads by five games to none or by four games to one; otherwise the series continues until one or the other has a lead of two games.

What is the probability that A wins the series?

4. The respective probabilities that a gambler wins or loses a bet are $\frac{3}{8}$ and $\frac{5}{8}$. If he makes a series of independent bets what is the probability that he will have a run of five consecutive wins before he has a run of three consecutive failures?

5. A golfer has respective probabilities $\frac{1}{3}$, $\frac{1}{6}$, $\frac{1}{2}$ of winning, halving or losing any hole he plays. Assuming all holes are independent and that he plays an indefinitely prolonged match, what is the probability that he has a run of three consecutive winning holes before any run of two consecutive losing holes?

6. From a pack of 52 playing cards a player draws a card at random, replaces it, shuffles the pack, makes another draw at random, replaces it and so on until he draws a king, queen or jack at which time the draws cease. Each time he draws an ace he receives a payment; no payment is made on drawing any other card.

If the payment received for drawing an ace at the nth draw is n shillings, calculate his initial expectation.

If, on the other hand, the payment on drawing his nth ace is k^n shillings where $0 < k < 4$, by establishing a relationship between his expectations before and after the first draw find his initial expectation.

7. If u_n is the probability that in n tosses of a symmetrical coin three or more consecutive heads do not turn up, show that for $n \geqslant 4$,

$$u_{n-1} - u_n = \tfrac{1}{16} u_{n-4},$$

and hence evaluate u_7.

8. A number of players take part in a competition for a trophy which is awarded annually. The players are of equal skill and the player who wins in any year is ineligible to compete in the following year. Show that the probability that the player who wins the trophy in the first year will win it again in the fifth year is greater by $\tfrac{25}{216}$ when there are three players than when there are four.

If there are m players, show, by constructing and solving a first order difference equation, that the probability that the player who wins in the first year will win again in the nth year is

$$\frac{1}{m} \left\{ 1 - \left(\frac{-1}{m-1} \right)^{n-2} \right\}, \qquad n \geqslant 2.$$

9. The respective probabilities of heads and tails when a biased coin is tossed are p and $1-p$. If u_n denotes the probability that two heads in succession do not occur in n trials, show that

$$u_{n+2} = (1-p)u_{n+1} + p(1-p)u_n.$$

Hence find the value of u_n when $p = \tfrac{2}{3}$.

10. If a day is dry the conditional probability that the following day will also be dry is p; if a day is wet, the conditional probability that the following day will be dry is p'. If u_n is the probability that the nth day will be dry, prove that

$$u_n - (p - p')u_{n-1} - p' = 0, \qquad n \geqslant 2.$$

If the first day is dry, $p = \frac{3}{4}$ and $p' = \frac{1}{4}$, find u_n.

11. Seven hotels A, B, C, D, E, F, G in order are located on a road which runs north-south with A the most northerly hotel. A motorist starts a tour from C and moves according to the following rules. Each day he throws a symmetrical die; if he throws 1, he travels to the nearest hotel to the north; if he throws 2 or 3, he travels to the nearest hotel to the south; if he throws 4, 5 or 6 he spends the day where he is. The tour ends when he reaches either A or G. What is the probability that the tour ends at A?

What is the expected number of days that the tour will last?

12. A teacher, with a class of r pupils, asks individual members of the class questions. For each question a pupil is selected at random subject to the condition that no pupil is asked two questions in succession. What is the probability that the pupil who is asked the first question is also asked the nth question?

If $r = 6$, what is the probability that the same child is asked the first, the third and the sixth questions?

13. Two players, A and B, play a series of independent games, their respective probabilities of winning any single game being $\frac{3}{4}$ and $\frac{1}{4}$. The series terminates when either A wins ten games more than B or when B wins four games more than A. What is the probability that A wins the series?

What is the probability of A winning the series without being led by B at any stage?

14. A tetrahedron which has three green faces and one red face is placed with one face in contact with a table. It

is then moved from its initial position by rotating it about one of the edges in contact with the table, all three edges being equally likely, until an adjacent face rests in contact with the table. A series of such moves is performed. If p_n denotes the probability that the red face is in contact with the table after n moves, show that

$$p_{n+1} = \tfrac{1}{3}(1-p_n)$$

and hence find p_n when initially (i) the red face and (ii) a green face was in contact with the table.

If the initial face in contact with the table was chosen at random from the four faces what is the probability that the red face will be in contact with the table after n moves?

15. A symmetrical six-sided die has its three pairs of opposite faces marked A, B and C respectively. It is thrown on to a flat table and the position it takes up is the initial state of the system. A move of the system consists of selecting at random one of the four edges in contact with the table and rotating the die through 90° about that edge. If a_n, b_n, c_n denote respectively the probabilities that after n moves a face marked A, B, C is uppermost, prove that

$$a_{n+1} = \tfrac{1}{2}b_n + \tfrac{1}{2}c_n,$$
$$a_n + b_n + c_n = 1,$$

and hence find a_n when (i) initially a face marked A was uppermost and (ii) initially the uppermost face was not marked A.

Show that as n tends to infinity these two probabilities tend to equality.

CHAPTER VI

RECURRENT EVENTS AND
RENEWAL PROCESSES

§43. Recurrent events. We now consider a series of repeated trials of a system having possible outcomes A_i $(i = 1, 2, 3, \ldots)$; in many cases, these trials will be independent, but this restriction is not necessary and will be missing from later examples. We assume that the series of trials may be regarded as possibly being continued indefinitely and that the probabilities of any possible joint outcome of the first n trials, such as $p\{A_{i_1}, A_{i_2}, \ldots, A_{i_n}\}$, are defined for all n. Associated with such a series of trials we can consider a type of event defined by certain repetitive patterns of trial outcomes. Such an event $\mathscr{E}$ is described as a **recurrent event** if for every possible joint outcome of n trials, such as $\{A_{i_1}, A_{i_2}, \ldots, A_{i_n}\}$, it can be uniquely determined whether or not $\mathscr{E}$ has occurred, and if it has occurred, then at which trial or trials. Furthermore, every time that $\mathscr{E}$ occurs, subsequent trials are effectively an exact replica of the complete sequence of trials. That is to say, once $\mathscr{E}$ has occurred, there is no carry over of any contribution towards a subsequent occurrence of $\mathscr{E}$.

For example, suppose that $\mathscr{E}$ denoted the sequence HHTH in repeated tossing of a coin. Then if the results of the first fifteen tosses were THTHHTHHTHHTHTT we see that the first completion of the pattern which defines $\mathscr{E}$ occurs at the seventh trial. When establishing subsequent occurrences of $\mathscr{E}$ we must allow no carry-over effect from the end of the pattern which established the first occurrence of $\mathscr{E}$. Thus a second occurrence of $\mathscr{E}$ does not take place at the tenth trial since the H at trial seven has been used to complete the pattern for the first occurrence. Further scrutiny of the results shows that it is not until the thirteenth trial that the second non-overlapping HHTH pattern is completed.

To ensure that there is no carry-over effect after $\mathscr{E}$ has happened, it follows that all events following an occurrence of $\mathscr{E}$ must be statistically independent of the outcomes of all trials up to and including that at which $\mathscr{E}$ occurred. We can now incorporate these conditions in a formal definition of a recurrent event.

$\mathscr{E}$ is a **recurrent event** associated with a series of trials if:

(i) for every sequence of outcomes $(A_{i_1}, A_{i_2}, \ldots, A_{i_n})$ there exists a rule, dependent only on that sequence and independent of subsequent outcomes, which uniquely determines whether or not $\mathscr{E}$ occurs at the last, that is the nth, trial of the sequence;

(ii) when $\mathscr{E}$ occurs at the last trial of the sequence $(A_{i_1}, A_{i_2}, \ldots, A_{i_n})$ then it occurs again at the last trial of the sequence $(A_{i_1}, A_{i_2}, \ldots, A_{i_n}, A_{j_1}, A_{j_2}, \ldots, A_{j_m})$ if and only if it occurs at the last trial of the sequence $(A_{j_1}, A_{j_2}, \ldots, A_{j_m})$;

(iii) when $\mathscr{E}$ occurs at the nth trial, the conditional probability that it occurs again at the $(m+n)$th trial is equal to the probability that it occurs at the mth trial.

§44. Classification of recurrent events. Recurrence times.

If we introduce the symbol f_i to denote the probability that

$\mathscr{E}$ occurs for the first time at the ith trial then we see that the probability that $\mathscr{E}$ happens in the first k trials is $f_1 + f_2 + f_3 + \ldots + f_k$.

When $\mathop{\mathrm{Lt}}\limits_{k \to \infty} \sum\limits_{i=1}^{k} f_i = 1$ we see that, in an unlimited sequence of trials, the probability that $\mathscr{E}$ occurs in the first k trials tends to 1 as k tends to infinity and we can describe $\mathscr{E}$ as being certain to happen. Then $\mathscr{E}$ is defined to be a **certain recurrent event**.

If $\sum\limits_{i=1}^{\infty} f_i < 1$, $\mathscr{E}$ is called an **uncertain recurrent event**. Certain and uncertain recurrent events are also described respectively as being **persistent** and **transient** events.

When the nature of $\mathscr{E}$ is such that it is only possible for it to occur at trials number $\alpha, 2\alpha, 3\alpha, \ldots (\alpha > 1)$, that is if $f_k = 0$ when $k \neq r\alpha$ where r is a positive integer and where α is the largest integer for which this property holds, then $\mathscr{E}$ is said to have **period** α. When $\alpha = 1$, it is possible for $\mathscr{E}$ to happen at any trial, and $\mathscr{E}$ is said to be an **aperiodic recurrent event**.

When $\mathscr{E}$ is certain, the number of trials up to and including that at which $\mathscr{E}$ first occurs is an integral-valued variate, x_1, say, having probability function

$$p_j = p(x_1 = j) = f_j, \quad j = 1, 2, 3, \ldots.$$

For later convenience we define f_0 to be 0.

This variate x_1 is the **first recurrence time** of $\mathscr{E}$. Similarly we can define the kth recurrence time of $\mathscr{E}$ as being the number of trials following the $(k-1)$th occurrence up to and including that at which the kth occurrence takes place. This time we may denote by x_k and, due to the definition of recurrent events, it follows that $x_1, x_2, \ldots, x_k, \ldots$ are independent integral valued variates which have identical probability functions.

Introducing the generating function $G(s) = \sum_{j=0}^{\infty} f_j s^j$ we have

$$G'(1) = \sum_{j=1}^{\infty} jf_j = \tau,$$

where τ is the arithmetic mean of each x_i and is called the **mean recurrence time** of the event $\mathscr{E}$. This time τ may be finite or infinite.

Associated with the individual recurrence times x_i is the integral-valued variate $S_n = \sum_{i=1}^{n} x_i$, which denotes the total number of trials up to and including that at which $\mathscr{E}$ occurs for the nth time. Results relating to the distribution of S_n can be examined by using the fact that its probability generating function is given by $[G(s)]^n$.

To summarise, we see that recurrent events are classified into certain (or persistent) and uncertain (or transient) events according as $\sum_{j=0}^{\infty} f_j = 1$ or $\sum_{j=0}^{\infty} f_j < 1$; the certain events are further divided into those with finite and infinite mean recurrence times. All classes are further subdivided into periodic and aperiodic.

If, for an uncertain event $\mathscr{E}$, we write $\sum_{j=0}^{\infty} f_j = f < 1$, then it follows that $(1-f)$ gives the probability that $\mathscr{E}$ does not occur at all. From the independence condition in the definition of $\mathscr{E}$ it follows that $f(1-f)$ is the probability that $\mathscr{E}$ will occur exactly once in an infinite series of trials; similarly $f^n(1-f)$ is the probability that $\mathscr{E}$ occurs exactly n times.

Thus $(1-f)(1+f+f^2+ \ldots +f^n) = 1-f^{n+1} = p(\mathscr{E}$ not more than n times). As $n \to \infty$, $f^{n+1} \to 0$ and thus it follows that the probability that an uncertain recurrent event will occur only a finite number of times in an infinitely prolonged sequence of trials is 1.

§45. Probabilities of recurrent events.

A second family of probabilities can be considered for recurrent events. Whereas f_j denoted the probability that the event $\mathscr{E}$ would occur for the first time at the jth trial, we define a_j to be the probability that $\mathscr{E}$ happens at the jth trial, not necessarily for the first time. From the addition and multiplication axioms it follows that the two sets of probabilities must satisfy the relation

$$a_j = f_j + a_1 f_{j-1} + a_2 f_{j-2} + \ldots + a_{j-1} f_1, \quad j \geqslant 1,$$

the terms on the right-hand side being probabilities of mutually exclusive joint events one of which must happen if $\mathscr{E}$ happens at the jth trial.

This relation enables successive calculation of the a_j when the f_j are known, and vice versa. If, for convenience, we define

$$a_0 = 1, \quad f_0 = 0,$$

we have the symmetric result

$$a_j = a_0 f_j + a_1 f_{j-1} + a_2 f_{j-2} + \ldots + a_j f_0, \quad j \geqslant 1.$$

If we now introduce the generating functions,

$$A(s) = \sum_{j=0}^{\infty} a_j s^j, \qquad G(s) = \sum_{j=0}^{\infty} f_j s^j,$$

then, multiplying the recurrence relation by s^j and summing both sides over the range $j = 1, 2, 3, \ldots$, we find that

$$A(s) - a_0 = A(s) \cdot G(s)$$

since the coefficients of s^j on the right-hand side are identifiable as being the convolution of the two sequences $\{a_j\}$ and $\{f_j\}$.

Then since $a_0 = 1$ we have the result

$$A(s) - 1 = A(s) \cdot G(s),$$

so that

$$A(s) = \frac{1}{1 - G(s)}.$$

Assuming that it is permissible to substitute 1 for s in this equation—it is possible to justify the procedure—we now have

$$\sum_{j=0}^{\infty} a_j = \frac{1}{1 - \sum_{j=0}^{\infty} f_j},$$

or

$$1 + \sum_{j=1}^{\infty} a_j = \frac{1}{1 - \sum_{j=1}^{\infty} f_j}.$$

Now, when $\mathscr{E}$ is certain, $\sum_{j=1}^{\infty} f_j = 1$ and hence for such events $\sum_{j=1}^{\infty} a_j$ must be divergent. When $\mathscr{E}$ is uncertain, we have $\sum_{j=1}^{\infty} f_j = f < 1$ and so

$$1 + \sum_{j=1}^{\infty} a_j = \frac{1}{1 - f},$$

from which it follows that for such events $\sum\limits_{j=1}^{\infty} a_j$ is convergent. So we have the result that $\mathscr{E}$ is certain or uncertain according as $\sum\limits_{j=1}^{\infty} a_j$ is divergent or convergent.

By noting that a_j can be regarded as the expected number of occurrences of $\mathscr{E}$ at the jth trial, since

$$a_j = 1 \cdot a_j + 0 \cdot (1 - a_j),$$

and that consequently

$$\sum\limits_{j=1}^{k} a_j = \text{Expected number of occurrences of } \mathscr{E} \text{ in } k \text{ trials},$$

it is seen that the above result is in accordance with general reasoning.

The probability that an uncertain recurrent event $\mathscr{E}$ happens is given by

$$f = \frac{\sum\limits_{j=1}^{\infty} a_j}{1 + \sum\limits_{j=1}^{\infty} a_j}.$$

§46. Limiting value of the probability a_n for certain recurrent events.

A result with many important applications is the following theorem.

If $\mathscr{E}$ is an aperiodic certain recurrent event having mean recurrence time $\tau = \sum\limits_{j=1}^{\infty} j f_j,$ *then*

$$a_n \to \frac{1}{\tau} \text{ as } n \to \infty.$$

When $\mathscr{E}$ is periodic with period $\alpha > 1$, then

$$a_{n\alpha} \to \frac{\alpha}{\tau} \text{ as } n \to \infty,$$

while

$$a_j = 0 \text{ for } j \neq r\alpha \text{ where } r \text{ is a positive integer.}$$

The elementary proof of this theorem is based on a theorem on power series proved by Erdös, Feller and Pollard in 1949. We shall establish the result for the aperiodic case and deduce the periodic result from this.

When $\mathscr{E}$ is certain and aperiodic, $f_0 = 0, f_j \geqslant 0, \sum_{j=0}^{\infty} f_j = 1$ and the highest common factor of those values of j for which $f_j > 0$ is 1.

We also know that

$$a_n = f_0 a_n + f_1 a_{n-1} + \ldots + f_n a_0, \quad n \geqslant 1. \qquad (1)$$

If we define

$$r_n = \sum_{j=n+1}^{\infty} f_j, \qquad (2)$$

it follows that

$$\sum_{n=0}^{\infty} r_n = \sum_{n=0}^{\infty} \sum_{j=n+1}^{\infty} f_j = \sum_{n=0}^{\infty} n f_n = \tau. \qquad (3)$$

From the given conditions and (2) it follows that

$$r_0 = 1, \quad f_1 = r_0 - r_1, \quad f_2 = r_1 - r_2, \ldots$$

which, on substitution in (1) gives

$$r_0 a_n + r_1 a_{n-1} + \ldots + r_n a_0 =$$
$$r_0 a_{n-1} + r_1 a_{n-2} + \ldots + r_{n-1} a_0, \quad n \geqslant 1.$$

Since this is true for all n, it follows that all terms of the convolution of the sequences $\{a_n\}$ and $\{r_n\}$ are equal. The first of these terms is $r_0 a_0$ and since we have shown that $r_0 = 1$ and have defined $a_0 = 1$, it follows that

$$r_0 a_n + r_1 a_{n-1} + \ldots + r_n a_0 = 1, \quad n \geqslant 0. \quad (4)$$

Also, since the a_n are probabilities, it is known that $0 \leqslant a_n \leqslant 1$, and so there must exist $\Lambda = \overline{\lim} \, a_n$ such that for $\varepsilon > 0$ and all sufficiently large n, $a_n < \Lambda + \varepsilon$ and there exists a sequence $n_1, n_2, n_3, \ldots$ such that $a_{n_k} \to \Lambda$ as $k \to \infty$.

Now, if j is any positive integer such that $f_j > 0$, we can establish that the sequence $a_{n_k - j} \to \Lambda$ as $k \to \infty$. To prove this, we examine the consequences of the assumption that the result is not true. Then it would be possible to find arbitrarily large subscripts n such that simultaneously

$$a_n > \Lambda - \varepsilon \quad \text{and} \quad a_{n-j} < \Lambda - \frac{3\varepsilon}{f_j}.$$

If N is large enough to ensure that $r_N < \varepsilon$, then using the facts that $0 \leqslant a_n \leqslant 1$, and that

$$a_n = f_0 a_n + f_1 a_{n-1} + f_2 a_{n-2} + \ldots \\ + f_N a_{n-N} + f_{N+1} a_{n-N-1} + \ldots + f_n a_0,$$

we have for $n > N$

$$a_n \leqslant f_0 a_n + f_1 a_{n-1} + \ldots + f_N a_{n-N} + f_{N+1} + f_{N+2} + \ldots + f_n.$$

Thus

$$a_n \leqslant f_0 a_n + f_1 a_{n-1} + \ldots + f_N a_{n-N} + r_N,$$

so that

$$a_n \leqslant f_0 a_n + f_1 a_{n-1} + \ldots + f_N a_{n-N} + \varepsilon.$$

For sufficiently large n, each a_i on the right-hand side is less that $\Lambda + \varepsilon$ and on our assumption $a_{n-j} < \Lambda - \dfrac{3\varepsilon}{f_j}$.

Hence

$$a_n < (f_0 + f_1 + \ldots + f_{j-1} + f_{j+1} + \ldots + f_N)\,(\Lambda + \varepsilon)$$
$$+ f_j\left(\Lambda - \frac{3\varepsilon}{f_j}\right) + \varepsilon,$$

and so

$$a_n < (1 - f_j)\,(\Lambda + \varepsilon) + f_j\left(\Lambda - \frac{3\varepsilon}{f_j}\right) + \varepsilon,$$
$$a_n < \Lambda + 2\varepsilon - 3\varepsilon - \varepsilon f_j,$$
$$a_n < \Lambda - \varepsilon.$$

But this contradicts the inequality $a_n > \Lambda - \varepsilon$ and hence we must reject the assumption that for sufficiently large n we could have

$$a_n > \Lambda - \varepsilon \quad \text{and} \quad a_{n-j} < \Lambda - \frac{3\varepsilon}{f_j}.$$

Thus we have established that whenever $a_{n_k} \to \Lambda$ then, when $f_j > 0$, $a_{n_k - j} \to \Lambda$ and by repeated application of this result it follows that then $a_{n_k - lj} \to \Lambda$ for all positive integral values of l.

Now let us first use this result to consider the special class of recurrent events for which $f_1 > 0$. Taking $j = 1$ we see that for such events this result shows that if $a_{n_k} \to \Lambda$ then $a_{n_k - l} \to \Lambda$ for any fixed positive integral value of l.

From (4) for $n = n_k$ it follows that

$$1 \geqslant r_0 a_{n_k} + r_1 a_{n_k - 1} + \ldots + r_N a_{n_k - N}. \tag{5}$$

For fixed N, since every $a_{n_k - l} \to \Lambda$, it then follows that

$$1 \geqslant \Lambda(r_0 + r_1 + \ldots + r_N)$$

and, since this is true for any fixed N, by using the result $\sum_{n=0}^{\infty} r_n = \tau$ we have $1 \geqslant \Lambda\tau$, and hence

$$\Lambda \leqslant \frac{1}{\tau}.$$

Now if τ is infinite, this result shows that $\Lambda \leqslant 0$. The bounded sequence $\{a_n\}$ has also a lower limit $\lambda = \underline{\lim}\ a_n$ and since $a_n \geqslant 0$ for all n, $\lambda \geqslant 0$, and finally since $\Lambda \geqslant \lambda$ it follows that when $f_1 > 0$ and τ is infinite,

$$\Lambda = \lambda = 0,$$

and

$$a_n \to \frac{1}{\tau}.$$

To complete the proof of the theorem when $f_1 > 0$ and τ is finite we observe that the same form of argument as that used for establishing the corresponding result for Λ can be used to show that for such events if $n_1, n_2, \ldots$ is a sequence such that $a_{n_k} \to \lambda$ as $k \to \infty$ then $a_{n_k - l} \to \lambda$ as $k \to \infty$ for any positive integer l.

When τ is finite, since $\sum_{n=0}^{\infty} r_n = \tau$, there must exist an integer N large enough to satisfy $\sum_{n=N+1}^{\infty} r_n < \varepsilon$, and then from (4) we have

$$1 \leqslant r_0 a_{n_k} + r_1 a_{n_k-1} + \ldots + r_N a_{n_k-N} + \varepsilon.$$

Since $a_{n_k - l} \to \lambda$ it follows that for all sufficiently large N

$$1 \leqslant (r_0 + r_1 + \ldots + r_N)\lambda + \varepsilon,$$

and hence

$$\tau\lambda \geqslant 1.$$

Again since $\lambda \leqslant \Lambda$, it follows that $\lambda = \Lambda = \dfrac{1}{\tau}$ and so

$a_n \to \dfrac{1}{\tau}$. Thus the theorem has been established for those $\mathscr{E}$ which are aperiodic with finite or infinite τ for which $f_1 > 0$.

We next extend the theorem to those aperiodic events for which $f_1 = 0$. When $\mathscr{E}$ is aperiodic, it is possible to find a finite number of integers $j_1, j_2, \ldots, j_m$ for which $f_{j_i} > 0$ and for which the highest common factor is unity. When $a_{n_k} \to \Lambda$ for such events, we have proved that

$$a_{n_k - l_1 j_1} \to \Lambda, \, a_{n_k - l_2 j_2} \to \Lambda, \, \ldots, \, a_{n_k - l_m j_m} \to \Lambda$$

where the l_i are positive integers, and hence that

$$a_{n_k - z} \to \Lambda$$

where $z = \sum_{i=1}^{m} l_i j_i$. But, since it is known from elementary number theory that any integer exceeding the product $\prod_{i=1}^{m} j_i$ can be expressed in the form $\sum_{i=1}^{m} l_i j_i$ where the l_i are non-negative integers, it follows that for all $z > \prod_{i=1}^{m} j_i$ we have

$a_{n_k - z} \to \Lambda$, and applying (4) with $n = n_k - \prod_{i=1}^{m} j_i$ to obtain the analogous inequality to (5) it is then possible to complete the proof with the same form of argument as was used for events with $f_1 > 0$.

Thus we have proved that for any aperiodic certain recurrent event

$$a_n \to \dfrac{1}{\tau}.$$

Finally we observe that when $\mathscr{E}$ has period α, only powers of s^α appear in $G(s)$, and $G(s^{1/\alpha})$ is thus a polynomial in s, say $\mathscr{G}(s)$. Furthermore, since $\mathscr{E}$ is certain, $\mathscr{G}(1) = 1$ and so we may consider $\mathscr{G}(s)$ as the generating function of a recurrent event to which the previous result applies. It follows that if

$$\mathscr{A}(s) = \frac{1}{1 - \mathscr{G}(s)}$$

then the coefficients of $\mathscr{A}(s)$ tend to $\dfrac{1}{T}$ where

$$T = \left[\frac{d\mathscr{G}(s)}{ds} \right]_{s=1} = \frac{1}{\alpha} \left[\frac{dG(s)}{ds} \right]_{s=1} = \frac{\tau}{\alpha}.$$

But the coefficient of s^n in $\mathscr{A}(s)$ is the coefficient of $s^{\alpha n}$ in $A(s)$ and the second part of the theorem relating to periodic events is thus established.

§47. Some examples of recurrent events.

(1) A series of independent games is played by two players A and B such that their respective probabilities of winning any single game are p and q, where $p + q = 1$. If such a series of games is continued without limit, then the event $\mathscr{E}$ that the accumulated numbers of wins recorded by the players are equal is a recurrent event with period 2.

The periodicity is self-evident and since the initial state recurs whenever $\mathscr{E}$ happens, the recurrent condition is satisfied.

From basic probability axioms it is seen that

$$a_{2n} = \binom{2n}{n} p^n q^n, \quad a_{2n+1} = 0.$$

Thus

$$A(s) = \sum_{n=0}^{\infty} \binom{2n}{n} p^n q^n s^{2n}$$

$$= (1 - 4pqs^2)^{-\frac{1}{2}}.$$

Hence

$$A(1) = \sum_{i=0}^{\infty} a_i = (1 - 4pq)^{-\frac{1}{2}},$$

and using the fact that $1 = (p+q)^2 = p^2 + 2pq + q^2$, we find that

$$A(1) = \frac{1}{|p-q|}.$$

Thus, provided $p \neq q$, $\sum_{i=0}^{\infty} a_i$ is convergent and hence, using the second result of §45, $\mathscr{E}$ is uncertain with probability $\dfrac{\{1/|p-q|\}-1}{1/|p-q|} = 1 - |p-q|$. In the special case $p = q = \frac{1}{2}$ it is seen that $\sum_{i=0}^{\infty} a_i$ is divergent and hence that $\mathscr{E}$ is certain. Furthermore, we have for this special case,

$$A(s) = (1 - s^2)^{-\frac{1}{2}}.$$

From §45, $\qquad G(s) = 1 - \dfrac{1}{A(s)} = 1 - (1 - s^2)^{\frac{1}{2}}.$

Thus

$$G'(s) = \frac{s}{(1 - s^2)^{\frac{1}{2}}},$$

and since τ = mean recurrence time = $G'(1)$ it follows that when $p = q = \frac{1}{2}$, $\mathscr{E}$ is a certain recurrent event with period 2 and infinite mean recurrence time.

(2) When a symmetrical die is thrown repeatedly, the event $\mathscr{E}$ that the accumulated numbers of ones, twos, ... and sixes are equal, is clearly recurrent with period 6.

We readily identify the probabilities

$$a_{6n} = \frac{(6n)!}{(n!)^6 6^{6n}}, \quad a_j = 0, \quad j \not\equiv 0 \;(\text{mod } 6).$$

Since $n! \sim \sqrt{(2\pi n)} \left(\frac{n}{e}\right)^n$ as $n \to \infty$, it follows that as $n \to \infty$,

$$a_{6n} \sim \frac{\sqrt{(12\pi n)} \left(\frac{6n}{e}\right)^{6n}}{(2\pi n)^{6/2} \left(\frac{n}{e}\right)^{6n} 6^{6n}},$$

$$a_{6n} \sim K n^{-5/2},$$

and hence that $\sum\limits_{n=0}^{\infty} a_{6n}$ is convergent. Thus $\mathscr{E}$ is uncertain. By numerical computation it is possible to evaluate this sum and, by using §45, to obtain the probability that $\mathscr{E}$ should ever happen.

(3) In a series of repeated independent Bernoulli trials with constant probability p of success and $q = 1-p$ of failure, the event $\mathscr{E}$ of a run of r consecutive successes is a recurrent event if it is agreed that once $\mathscr{E}$ has happened, only further successes are counted towards the next occurrence of $\mathscr{E}$, there being no carry-over effect.

If a_n denotes the probability that $\mathscr{E}$ occurs at the nth trial, not necessarily for the first time, then by considering the probability that the sequence of trials $n-r+1, n-r+2, \ldots, n$ all result in successes we see that

$$a_{n-r+1}p^{r-1} + a_{n-r+2}p^{r-2} + \ldots + a_{n-1}p + a_n = p^r, \quad n \geqslant r,$$

since the right-hand term is the probability of r consecutive successes at all these trials, while the left-hand terms are the probabilities of mutually exclusive joint events of the type $\mathscr{E}$ happens at trial $n-k$ followed by k subsequent successes, and one of these joint events must happen if the r consecutive successes take place.

Multiplying this relation by s^n and summing the resulting equations for $n = r, r+1, r+2, \ldots$ we have, since $a_0 = 1$ and $a_1 = a_2 = \ldots = a_{r-1} = 0$,

$$(a_r s^r + a_{r+1}s^{r+1} + \ldots)(1 + ps + p^2 s^2 + \ldots + p^{r-1}s^{r-1})$$
$$= p^r s^r (1 + s + s^2 + \ldots),$$

$$\frac{(A(s) - 1)(1 - p^r s^r)}{(1 - ps)} = \frac{p^r s^r}{(1 - s)},$$

$$A(s) = \frac{p^r s^r - p^{r+1}s^{r+1} + 1 - s - p^r s^r + p^r s^{r+1}}{(1-s)(1-p^r s^r)}$$

$$= \frac{1 - s + qp^r s^{r+1}}{(1-s)(1-p^r s^r)}.$$

If, as usual, $G(s)$ is the generating function for the first occurrence or recurrence time probabilities $\{f_n\}$ then

$$G(s) = 1 - \frac{1}{A(s)} = \frac{p^r s^r (1 - ps)}{1 - s + qp^r s^{r+1}},$$

from which the recurrence time distribution properties may be studied.

(4) If a physical system is capable of being in one of n states $S_1, S_2, \ldots, S_n$ and if as the result of a trial of the system it may change its state according to the constant transition probabilities

p_{ij} = Probability that as the result of a trial the system changes from S_j to S_i,

then whenever an S_i occurs the subsequent occurrence of S_i is a recurrent event. We shall examine the properties of such systems in the next chapter which deals with Markov chains. We note that since any trial must result in the system being in one of its possible states, the transition probabilities satisfy

$$\sum_{i=1}^{n} p_{ij} = 1, \qquad j = 1, 2, 3, \ldots, n.$$

§48. Renewal processes.

The basic results of §§46 and 47 can be extended to cover renewal processes which include recurrent event theory as a special case.

If we consider the recurrence relations

$$a_n = b_n + (h_0 a_n + h_1 a_{n-1} + \ldots + h_n a_0), \quad n \geqslant 0,$$

where $\{h_n\}$ and $\{b_n\}$ are given bounded sequences of non-negative numbers with $h_0 \neq 1$, then it is possible to solve successively to obtain the unique solution for the sequence $\{a_n\}$. We shall examine, under certain restrictions, the limiting behaviour of a_n. [It can be seen that in the particular case when $b_0 = 1$, $b_n = 0$ for $n \geqslant 1$ and $\{h_n\} = \{f_n\}$ the above recurrence equation is that for the two families of probabilities in recurrent event theory.]

Multiplying the recurrence equation by s^n and summing for $n = 0, 1, 2, \ldots$ we obtain

$$A(s) = B(s) + H(s) A(s),$$

$$A(s) = \frac{B(s)}{1 - H(s)},$$

where $A(s)$, $B(s)$ and $H(s)$ are the generating functions of the corresponding sequences. If all $h_n = 0$ for $n \neq r\alpha$ where r is a positive integer and α is a positive integer > 1, giving $H(s)$ as a power series in s^α, and if α is the largest integer with this property, we describe the process as being periodic with period α. We now establish certain results regarding the limiting value of a_n for the special case when $B(1)$ is finite and $h_0 < 1$.

(i) *If $\{h_n\}$ forms a discrete probability function, that is*

$$H(1) = \sum_{n=0}^{\infty} h_n = 1,$$

and if $\{h_n\}$ is aperiodic, then as $n \to \infty$,

$$a_n \to \frac{B(1)}{\tau},$$

where

$$\tau = \sum_{n=0}^{\infty} n h_n = H'(1).$$

As a corollary it follows that $a_n \to 0$ when $\sum_{n=0}^{\infty} n h_n$ is divergent.

If u_n is the coefficient of s^n in $\dfrac{1}{1 - H(s)}$ then by the result established in §46 it follows that $u_n \to \dfrac{1}{\tau}$ as $n \to \infty$.

Defining $\quad U(s) = \sum_{n=0}^{\infty} u_n s^n = \dfrac{1}{1-H(s)}\quad$ we have

$$A(s) = \frac{B(s)}{1-H(s)} = B(s)\,U(s),$$

from which it follows that

$$a_n = u_n b_0 + u_{n-1} b_1 + \ldots + u_0 b_n.$$

When $\sum_{n=0}^{\infty} h_n = 1$ it is seen by comparison with §45 that the sequence $\{u_n\}$ must satisfy $0 \leqslant u_n \leqslant 1$. From this it follows that because $B(1)$ is finite, that is $\sum_{i=0}^{\infty} b_i$ is convergent, then for any $\varepsilon > 0$, there exists a sufficiently large integer N such that, for all integers $n > N$,

$$a_n - (u_n b_0 + u_{n-1} b_1 + \ldots + u_{n-N} b_N) < \varepsilon.$$

Since for any fixed k, $u_{n-k} b_k \to \dfrac{b_k}{\tau}$ as $n \to \infty$ it follows that

$$(u_n b_0 + u_{n-1} b_1 + \ldots + u_{n-N} b_N) \to \frac{\sum_{i=0}^{N} b_i}{\tau} \text{ as } n \to \infty.$$

Finally, letting $N \to \infty$, it follows that

$$a_n \to \frac{\sum_{i=0}^{\infty} b_i}{\tau} = \frac{B(1)}{\tau} \text{ as } n \to \infty.$$

(ia) *In the periodic case with period α, if*

$$H(1) = \sum_{n=0}^{\infty} h_n = 1$$

each of the α subsequences $\{a_{n\alpha+j}\}$, *where* $j = 0, 1, 2, \ldots,$ $(\alpha-1)$, *of* $\{a_n\}$ *has limit* $\dfrac{\alpha B_j(1)}{\tau}$ *as* $n \to \infty$,

where

$$B_j(1) = b_j + b_{\alpha+j} + b_{2\alpha+j} + \ldots.$$

The proof of this result will be found in *An Introduction to Probability Theory and its Applications*, Volume I, by W. Feller.

(ii) *If* $H(1) = \sum\limits_{n=0}^{\infty} h_n < 1$ *then* $\sum\limits_{n=0}^{\infty} a_n$ *is convergent.*

Since $A(s) = \dfrac{B(s)}{1-H(s)}$, and since we are only concerned with the case when $\sum\limits_{i=0}^{\infty} b_i = B(1)$ is finite, it follows that since $1-H(1) \neq 0$ we see that

$$A(1) = \frac{B(1)}{1-H(1)}$$

must be finite.

Thus $\sum\limits_{n=0}^{\infty} a_n$ must be convergent, since all a_n are non-negative when $h_0 < 1$.

(iii) *If* $\{h_n\}$ *is aperiodic and* $H(1) = \sum\limits_{n=0}^{\infty} h_n > 1$, *and if* $s = z$ *is the unique positive root of the equation* $H(s) = 1$, *then*

$$a_n z^n \to \frac{B(z)}{zH'(z)} \text{ as } n \to \infty.$$

Since $H(s)$ is a polynomial in s with non-negative co-efficients with $H(0) = h_0 < 1$ and $H(1) = \sum\limits_{n=0}^{\infty} h_n > 1$, it follows that a unique value z exists in the interval $(0, 1)$ such that $H(z) = 1$.

Now apply result (i) of this section to the coefficients of the power series in

$$A(zs) = \frac{B(zs)}{1 - H(zs)}$$

which are $\{a_n z^n\}$, $\{b_n z^n\}$ and $\{h_n z^n\}$ and it follows that

$$a_n z^n \to \frac{B(z)}{zH'(z)} \text{ as } n \to \infty.$$

Since $0 < z < 1$ this implies that a_n increases without limit since $B(z) < B(1)$ which is finite, and $H'(z)$ is finite since $H(s)$ is convergent for $0 < s < 1$.

§49. Example of renewal process.

In practice one often encounters "populations" of elements which have a finite effective life and which, on becoming ineffective, must immediately be replaced by new elements of the same kind. The total population size remains constant, and the important practical property is the number of elements which require to be replaced at future time intervals. To examine this, we must know the initial population size and "age" distribution, together with the probability function for the life span of a new element. A simple example is the population of electric light bulbs in a large office block or factory.

It will be assumed that sufficient accuracy can be attained by dividing future time into suitable finite intervals, and so we can regard the age of an element as being a discrete variate with a given probability function which we denote by $\{h_n\}$. We assume that at time 0 the initial population consists of $N = \sum_{k=0}^{\infty} l_k$ elements where l_k is the number of elements of exact age k. Each of the N elements will have a probability that it requires to be replaced at the end of the nth time interval (either for the first or for a subsequent time) and the total of these N probabilities gives a_n, the expected number of replacements at time n. It is reasonable to assume that $a_0 = 0$, and that $h_0 = 0$, i.e., the electric bulbs used have all been previously tested to ensure that they are not initially defective.

Replacements required at time n fall into two categories. They may consist of replacements of elements installed after time 0, i.e, at time j where $1 \leqslant j < n$, or they may consist of first replacements of elements of the initial population. The expected number of replacements at time j is a_j, and therefore the expected number of replacements of first type at time n must be

$$a_1 h_{n-1} + a_2 h_{n-2} + a_3 h_{n-3} + \ldots + a_{n-1} h_1.$$

To find the expected number of second type replacements at time n we must observe that the conditional probability that an element which has reached age k at time 0 will die at age $n+k$ at time n is given by

$$\frac{h_{k+n}}{h_{k+1} + h_{k+2} + h_{k+3} + \ldots} = \frac{h_{k+n}}{r_k}$$

where $r_k = h_{k+1} + h_{k+2} + h_{k+3} + \ldots =$ probability of surviving beyond age k. Hence, since there were l_k elements of age k in the initial population, the expected number of second type replacements at time n must be $\sum_{k=0}^{\infty} l_k \dfrac{h_{k+n}}{r_k}$ for $n > 0$ and we denote this by b_n. Noticing that we must define $b_0 = 0$, we see finally that the expected number of replacements satisfies the renewal equation of §48,

$$a_n = b_n + (h_0 a_n + h_1 a_{n-1} + \ldots + h_{n-1} a_1 + h_n a_0), \quad n \geqslant 0,$$

where $\{h_n\}$ and $\{b_n\}$ are bounded sequences of non-negative numbers and where

$$B(1) = \sum_{n=0}^{\infty} b_n =$$

$$\sum_{n=0}^{\infty} \sum_{k=0}^{\infty} l_k \frac{h_{k+n}}{r_k} = \sum_{k=0}^{\infty} l_k \left\{ \frac{h_{k+1} + h_{k+2} + \ldots}{r_k} \right\} = \sum_{k=0}^{\infty} l_k = N$$

which is finite.

It is therefore possible to apply the results of §48 to examine the limiting properties of a_n.

Also of interest is the age distribution of elements in the population at time n. Denoting by $l_k(n)$ the expected number of age k elements at time n, we have for $n > k$

$$l_k(n) = a_{n-k} \times \text{probability of survival to age at least } k$$

$$= a_{n-k} \times \{h_{k+1} + h_{k+2} + \ldots\}$$

$$= a_{n-k} r_k,$$

and for $n \leqslant k$

$$l_k(n) = l_{k-n} \times \text{probability of survival of an age } (k-n) \text{ element to age at least } k$$

$$= l_{k-n} \times \frac{h_{k+1} + h_{k+2} + \ldots}{h_{k-n+1} + h_{k-n+2} + \ldots}$$

$$= l_{k-n} \frac{r_k}{r_{k-n}}.$$

Since, in the aperiodic case, from §48 we have

$$a_n \to \frac{B(1)}{\tau} = N/\sum_{i=0}^{\infty} r_i,$$

it follows that

$$l_k(n) \to N r_k /\sum_{i=0}^{\infty} r_i \quad \text{as } n \to \infty,$$

and that if τ is infinite, the population ages without limit. We note that the limiting age distribution is independent of the initial population l_k and depends only on the sequence $\{r_k\}$, that is on the basic sequence $\{h_k\}$, and on the total population size N.

To illustrate the theory let us consider an initial population of elements $l_0 = 312$, $l_1 = 180$, $l_2 = 72$, $l_3 = 36$, having life span probabilities given by

$$h_0 = 0, \ h_1 = \tfrac{2}{3}, \ h_2 = \tfrac{1}{12}, \ h_3 = \tfrac{1}{6}, \ h_4 = \tfrac{1}{12}.$$

The total population size $N = \sum_{k=0}^{\infty} l_k = 600$; and we verify that $\sum_{k=0}^{\infty} h_k = 1$, and notice that no element will remain "alive" after reaching age 4.

The mean life span $\tau = \sum_{k=0}^{\infty} k h_k = 1 \cdot \tfrac{2}{3} + 2 \cdot \tfrac{1}{12} + 3 \cdot \tfrac{1}{6} + 4 \cdot \tfrac{1}{12} = 1\tfrac{2}{3}$ and so, by result (i) of §48, it follows that

$$a_n \to \frac{N}{\tau} = \frac{600}{1\tfrac{2}{3}} = 360 \text{ as } n \to \infty.$$

By summation of the h_k we obtain

$$r_0 = 1, \ r_1 = \tfrac{1}{3}, \ r_2 = \tfrac{1}{4}, \ r_3 = \tfrac{1}{12}, \ r_4 = 0$$

and since as $n \to \infty$, $l_k(n) = a_{n-k} r_k$ it follows that the limiting expected age distribution must be

$$l_0(\infty) = 360, \; l_1(\infty) = 120, \; l_2(\infty) = 90,$$
$$l_3(\infty) = 30, \; l_4(\infty) = 0.$$

To examine the expected age distribution for small values of n we form the generating function $A(s) = \sum\limits_{k=0}^{\infty} a_k s^k$ and pick out the necessary values of a_n as the coefficients in the expansion of $A(s)$. Since

$$A(s) = \frac{B(s)}{1 - H(s)}$$

we must obtain the values of b_k and hence $B(s) = \sum\limits_{k=0}^{\infty} b_k s^k$:

$b_0 = 0$ by definition.

$$b_1 = \sum_{i=0}^{\infty} \frac{l_i}{r_i} h_{1+i}$$

$$= \frac{l_0}{r_0} h_1 + \frac{l_1}{r_1} h_2 + \frac{l_2}{r_2} h_3 + \frac{l_3}{r_3} h_4$$

$$= 312 \times \tfrac{2}{3} + 540 \times \tfrac{1}{12} + 288 \times \tfrac{1}{6} + 432 \times \tfrac{1}{12} = 337.$$

$$b_2 = \sum_{i=0}^{\infty} \frac{l_i}{r_i} h_{2+i} = \frac{l_0}{r_0} h_2 + \frac{l_1}{r_1} h_3 + \frac{l_2}{r_2} h_4$$

$$= 312 \times \tfrac{1}{12} + 540 \times \tfrac{1}{6} + 288 \times \tfrac{1}{12} = 140.$$

$$b_3 = \sum_{i=0}^{\infty} \frac{l_i}{r_i} h_{3+i} = \frac{l_0}{r_0} h_3 + \frac{l_1}{r_1} h_4$$

$$= 312 \times \tfrac{1}{6} + 540 \times \tfrac{1}{12} = 97.$$

$$b_4 = \sum_{i=0}^{\infty} \frac{l_i}{r_i} h_{4+i} = \frac{l_0}{r_0} h_4$$

$$= 312 \times \tfrac{1}{12} = 26.$$

Hence we have

$$A(s) = \frac{337s + 140s^2 + 97s^3 + 26s^4}{1 - \frac{2}{3}s - \frac{1}{12}s^2 - \frac{1}{6}s^3 - \frac{1}{12}s^4}$$

$$= 12s \left\{ \frac{337 + 140s + 97s^2 + 26s^3}{(1-s)(3+s)(4+s^2)} \right\}$$

$$= 12s \left\{ \frac{30}{1-s} + \frac{\frac{22}{13}}{3+s} + \frac{\frac{30}{13}s - \frac{129}{13}}{4+s^2} \right\}$$

$$= 360s(1-s)^{-1} + \frac{88}{13}s\left(1 + \frac{s}{3}\right)^{-1}$$

$$\quad + \frac{3s}{13}(30s - 129)\left(1 + \frac{s^2}{4}\right)^{-1}$$

$$= 360s(1 + s + s^2 + \ldots) + \frac{88}{13}s\left(1 - \frac{s}{3} + \frac{s^2}{9} - \ldots\right)$$

$$\quad + \frac{3s}{13}(30s - 129)\left(1 - \frac{s^2}{4} + \frac{s^4}{16} - \ldots\right),$$

and by picking out coefficients we find

$$a_1 = 337 \cdot 0, \qquad a_2 = 364 \cdot 7, \qquad a_3 = 368 \cdot 2,$$
$$a_4 = 358 \cdot 0, \qquad a_5 = 358 \cdot 2, \qquad a_6 = 360 \cdot 4,$$
$$a_7 = 360 \cdot 5, \ldots$$

Substituting these values and the values for r_k and l_k in the formulae

$$l_k(n) = \begin{cases} a_{n-k}r_k & \text{for } n > k \\ l_{k-n}\dfrac{r_k}{r_{k-n}} & \text{for } n \leqslant k \end{cases}$$

we obtain the following table of values.

Values of $l_k(n)$

	n	0	1	2	3	4	5	6	7	....	∞
	0	312	337	364·7	368·2	358·0	358·2	360·4	360·5	....	360
k	1	180	104	112·3	121·6	122·7	119·3	119·4	120·1	....	120
	2	72	135	78	84·2	91·2	92·1	89·5	89·6	....	90
	3	36	24	45	26	28·1	30·4	30·7	29·8	....	30

We see that in this process the limiting expected age distribution is soon approximately attained. We also note that the result $a_n \to 360$ as $n \to \infty$ can be easily verified from the expansion of $A(s)$ since the contributions to the coefficient of s^n from the second and third partial fractions become negligible as $n \to \infty$.

EXERCISES VI

1. A symmetrical six-sided die with faces numbered 1, 2, 3, 4, 5, 6 is thrown repeatedly. Recurrent events $\mathscr{E}_1$, $\mathscr{E}_2$, $\mathscr{E}_3$, $\mathscr{E}_4$ are defined as follows:

$\mathscr{E}_1$ occurs whenever the face numbered 1 appears;

$\mathscr{E}_2$ occurs whenever the total numbers of appearances of even numbered faces and odd numbered faces are equal;

$\mathscr{E}_3$ occurs whenever the total number of appearances of 1, 2, 3 or 4 is equal to twice the total number of appearances of 5 or 6;

$\mathscr{E}_4$ occurs whenever each face has appeared the same total number of times.

Examine the nature of each event and find the mean recurrence times of those which are certain.

2. Two players A and B play a series of independent games in which their respective probabilities of winning any single game are $\frac{1}{3}$ and $\frac{2}{3}$. An event $\mathscr{E}$ occurs whenever the accumulated numbers of wins by A and B are equal. Show that $\mathscr{E}$ is a periodic, uncertain, recurrent event and find the probability that it ever happens.

Prove that

$$f_{2r} = \binom{2r-2}{r-1} \frac{2^{r+1}}{3^{2r}} \frac{1}{r}.$$

3. Starting from the origin, a particle is equally likely to move one unit north, east, south or west. The move is repeated, under similar conditions, from the new position and so on indefinitely, all moves being independent of one another. The event $\mathscr{E}$ happens when the particle returns to the origin. Show that $\mathscr{E}$ is recurrent, find the value of a_n and hence examine the nature of $\mathscr{E}$.

4. If z_r denotes the number of times that a recurrent event happens in r trials, prove that the expected values of z_r and z_r^2 are respectively,

$$a_1 + a_2 + \ldots + a_r,$$
$$a_1 + a_2 + \ldots + a_r + 2 \sum_{j=1}^{r-1} a_j(a_1 + \ldots + a_{r-j}),$$

and hence that they are given respectively by the coefficients of s^r in

$$\frac{G(s)}{(1-s)\{1-G(s)\}} \quad \text{and} \quad \frac{G^2(s)+G(s)}{(1-s)\{1-G(s)\}^2}.$$

5. If $\mathscr{E}$ is a recurrent event for which $f_0 = 0$, $f_j = (\frac{1}{3})^j$ for $j > 0$, and z denotes the number of times $\mathscr{E}$ happens in the first four trials, show that the approximate values of the mean and the variance of z are respectively $0{\cdot}802$ and $0{\cdot}973$.

6. A population consists of N individuals initially all aged zero. When an individual dies it is immediately replaced by a new individual aged zero. The lifetime of each individual is an integral valued variate with probability function $\{p_k\}$ where $p_0 = 0$ and $p_k = p(1-p)^{k-1}$ for $k = 1$, 2, 3, ... Find the expected number of replacements at time n and the limiting age distribution.

7. A population of 1000 individuals initially consists of 500 aged zero, 300 aged exactly 1, and 200 aged exactly 2. On death an individual is immediately replaced by a new individual aged zero. The lifetime of each individual has probability function $\{p_k\}$ where

$$p_0 = 0, p_1 = \tfrac{1}{12}, p_2 = \tfrac{3}{4}, p_3 = \tfrac{1}{6}, p_k = 0 \text{ for } k > 3.$$

Find the expected age distributions of the population at times 1, 2, 3, 4 and ∞.

8. An infinite sequence of positive numbers $\{u_n\}$ is defined by

$$u_{n+4} = \tfrac{1}{4}(u_n + u_{n+1} + u_{n+2} + u_{n+3}), \quad n \geqslant 1,$$

where u_1, u_2, u_3, u_4 are given positive numbers.
Prove that as $n \to \infty$

$$u_n \to \tfrac{1}{10}(u_1 + 2u_2 + 3u_3 + 4u_4).$$

CHAPTER VII

MARKOV CHAINS

§**50. Markov chains.** In a finite set of independent trials of a system it is known by the simple multiplication axiom (see §5) that the joint probability of a possible set of outcomes or events is given by the product of their respective individual probabilities, i.e.,

$$p(E_{\alpha_1} E_{\alpha_2} \ldots E_{\alpha_k}) = p(E_{\alpha_1}) \, p(E_{\alpha_2}) \ldots p(E_{\alpha_k}).$$

The simplest type of generalisation which can be made of independent trials is to allow the probabilities of the different possible outcomes of any trial to depend on the outcome of the immediately preceding trial, but on no others. For such a series of trials the probability of outcome E_{α_r} at the rth trial is not unique and initially known but is conditional on the actual outcome $E_{\alpha_{r-1}}$ which is obtained at the $(r-1)$th trial. Under this new dependence

$$p(E_{\alpha_1} E_{\alpha_2} \ldots E_{\alpha_k}) = \\ p(E_{\alpha_1}) \, p(E_{\alpha_2} \mid E_{\alpha_1}) \, p(E_{\alpha_3} \mid E_{\alpha_2}) \ldots p(E_{\alpha_k} \mid E_{\alpha_{k-1}}).$$

To define the probabilities of different sets of joint outcomes it is therefore seen that two families of probabilities must be known. First there is the initial probability distribution which governs the outcome of the first trial, and secondly there is the family of conditional, or, as they are called in this context, **transition probabilities** $p(E_{\alpha_r} \mid E_{\alpha_{r-1}})$ for all possible pairs of outcomes, not excluding the case when $\alpha_r = \alpha_{r-1}$, that is $E_{\alpha_r} \equiv E_{\alpha_{r-1}}$. A series of trials subject to this specialised type of dependence is called a **Markov chain**. In general, the transition probability $p(E_{\alpha_r} \mid E_{\alpha_{r-1}})$ is "time" dependent in the sense that it is a function of r, the number of the trial to which it refers. That is to say $p(E_i$ at rth trial $\mid E_j$ at $(r-1)$th trial) is not in general equal to $p(E_i$ at nth trial $\mid E_j$ at $(n-1)$th trial) when $r \neq n$. However many examples of practical interest have the simplification that transition probabilities are constant and we shall confine our attention to Markov chains with constant transition probabilities.

If we denote the initial probabilities by $p(E_j) = p_j$ where $j = 0, 1, 2, \ldots$ and the transition probabilities by $p(E_i \mid E_j) = p_{ij}$ where $i, j = 0, 1, 2, \ldots$ then we must have the natural conditions

$$p_j \geqslant 0, \quad \sum_j p_j = 1, \quad p_{ij} \geqslant 0, \quad \sum_i p_{ij} = 1,$$

the last arising from the consideration that at a trial following the appearance of E_j, some E_i must result.†

Two families of associated probabilities are of interest. First there are the higher transition probabilities, $p_{ij}^{(n)}$, defined as the conditional probability of obtaining E_i at the $(r+n)$th trial if E_j was obtained at the rth trial; for chains with constant transition probabilities these are independent of r. Thus

$$p_{ij}^{(1)} = p_{ij},$$
$$p_{ij}^{(2)} = \sum_k p_{ik} p_{kj},$$

† It should be noted that some books use the symbol p_{ij} to denote the probability of transition from the state E_i to E_j.

and in general

$$p_{ij}^{(n)} = \sum_k p_{ik} p_{kj}^{(n-1)}.$$

It can be easily verified that these probabilities also satisfy

$$p_{ij}^{(m+n)} = \sum_k p_{ik}^{(m)} p_{kj}^{(n)}.$$

In examining the behaviour of particular chains it is of fundamental interest to find whether $p_{ij}^{(n)}$ tends to a limit as $n \to \infty$, and if so whether this limit is independent of j.

Secondly there are the absolute probabilities $p_i^{(n)}$ defined as the total probability that E_i is obtained at the nth trial where we count trials subsequent to the initial state. (When a trial is needed to determine this initial state, it will be regarded as the zero trial.) Clearly we must have

$$p_i^{(n)} = \sum_j p_j p_{ij}^{(n)}$$

and it follows that if all $p_{ij}^{(n)}$ tend to limits as $n \to \infty$ for all j, then $p_i^{(n)}$ will also tend to a limit, being a weighted average of the limiting values of $p_{ij}^{(n)}$. Moreover, if for any i the $p_{ij}^{(n)}$ have a common limiting value, independent of j, then since $\sum_j p_j = 1$ it follows that $p_i^{(n)}$ will tend to this common limit. The significance of this last result is that the probability of obtaining E_i at the nth trial as $n \to \infty$ then tends to a limit which is independent of the initial probability distribution $\{p_j\}$.

§51. **Matrix form of transition probabilities.** It is convenient at this stage to modify our description of the chain to one which is more suitable to most actual applications. We are generally concerned with some physical system which can be in states E_1, E_2, E_3, ... and which at each "trial" may change from the state it is in, say E_j, to the state E_i (which of course could include $i = j$ when there is no change) with transition probability p_{ij}. We can conveniently represent the initial probability distribution by the column vector $\mathbf{p} = \{p_1, p_2, \ldots\}$ and the transition probabilities by the matrix $P = [p_{ij}]$.

By examining the product

$$P\mathbf{p} = \begin{bmatrix} p_{11} & p_{12} & p_{13} \cdots \\ p_{21} & p_{22} & p_{23} \cdots \\ p_{31} & p_{32} & p_{33} \cdots \\ \cdots\cdots\cdots\cdots \\ \cdots\cdots\cdots\cdots \end{bmatrix} \begin{bmatrix} p_1 \\ p_2 \\ p_3 \\ \vdots \\ \vdots \end{bmatrix} = \begin{bmatrix} \sum_k p_{1k}p_k \\ \sum_k p_{2k}p_k \\ \sum_k p_{3k}p_k \\ \vdots \\ \vdots \end{bmatrix}$$

we readily identify the elements in the resulting column vector as being $p_i^{(1)}$, the set of probabilities of the system being in the different states after one transition. Repetition of this operation shows that

$$P^2\mathbf{p} = \{p_i^{(2)}\}, \ P^3\mathbf{p} = \{p_i^{(3)}\}, \ldots, \ P^n\mathbf{p} = \{p_i^{(n)}\}.$$

Furthermore, from the last of these results it is seen that

$$p_i^{(n)} = \sum_k n_{ik}p_k,$$

where n_{ik} is the (i, k)th element of P^n, but since we have already established that

$$p_i^{(n)} = \sum_k p_{ik}^{(n)}p_k$$

it follows that $n_{ik} = p_{ik}^{(n)}$. That is to say if $P = [p_{ij}]$ then

$P^n = [p_{ij}^{(n)}]$, and so it is possible to examine the behaviour of transition and absolute probabilities as $n \to \infty$ by investigating the properties of the nth power of the matrix of transition probabilities.

As we have already noted, $p_{ij} \geqslant 0$ and $\sum_i p_{ij} = 1$, so we see that the matrix of transition probabilities, P, is a matrix with non-negative elements and unit column totals. Such a matrix is called a **stochastic matrix**, and, since i, j both range over the same values, it is a square matrix. In most of the examples to which we refer the system will have a finite number of possible states, say m, when P will be a matrix of order $m \times m$; but infinite examples do exist. For a special type of chain we may also have the condition $\sum_j p_{ij} = 1$, that is row sums are also unity. P is then called **doubly stochastic** and the associated chain has certain special properties.

The vector of absolute probabilities $\{p_i^{(n)}\}$ is given by

$$\{p_i^{(n)}\} = P^n\{p_i\}.$$

When $\lambda_1, \lambda_2, \ldots, \lambda_m$, the latent roots of P, are non-zero and all distinct, then from matrix theory it is known that we can express P in the form

$$P = H\Lambda H^{-1}$$

where

$$\Lambda = \operatorname{diag} \lambda_i = \begin{bmatrix} \lambda_1 & \cdot & \cdot & \cdot \cdots & \cdot & \cdot \\ \cdot & \lambda_2 & \cdot & \cdot \cdots & \cdot & \cdot \\ \cdot & \cdot & \lambda_3 & \cdot \cdots & \cdot & \cdot \\ \cdots\cdots\cdots\cdots\cdots\cdots\cdots \\ \cdot & \cdot & \cdot & \cdot \cdots & \lambda_{m-1} & \cdot \\ \cdot & \cdot & \cdot & \cdot \cdots & \cdot & \lambda_m \end{bmatrix}$$

and H is the matrix with columns given by the m latent column vectors of P, written in order.[†]

From this it follows that

$$\{p_i^{(n)}\} = (H\Lambda H^{-1})^n \{p_i\}$$
$$= H\Lambda^n H^{-1} \{p_i\}$$

where $\Lambda^n = \operatorname{diag} \lambda_i^n$, and so the problem of finding $p_{ij}^{(n)}$ and $p_i^{(n)}$ becomes that of finding latent roots and associated latent column vectors of P.

Example 7.1. Find the higher transition probabilities and the absolute probabilities for the system which starts in E_1 and has possible states E_1, E_2 and E_3 with transition probabilities given by the matrix

$$P = \begin{bmatrix} \frac{1}{2} & \frac{1}{4} & \frac{1}{6} \\ \frac{1}{3} & \frac{1}{2} & \frac{1}{3} \\ \frac{1}{6} & \frac{1}{4} & \frac{1}{2} \end{bmatrix}.$$

The latent roots of P are given by

$$\begin{aligned} |P - \lambda I| &= \begin{vmatrix} \frac{1}{2}-\lambda & \frac{1}{4} & \frac{1}{6} \\ \frac{1}{3} & \frac{1}{2}-\lambda & \frac{1}{3} \\ \frac{1}{6} & \frac{1}{4} & \frac{1}{2}-\lambda \end{vmatrix} \\ &= \tfrac{1}{18} - \tfrac{5}{9}\lambda + \tfrac{3}{2}\lambda^2 - \lambda^3 \\ &= (1-\lambda)(\tfrac{1}{3}-\lambda)(\tfrac{1}{6}-\lambda) = 0 \end{aligned}$$

So the latent roots are $\lambda_1 = 1$, $\lambda_2 = \frac{1}{3}$, $\lambda_3 = \frac{1}{6}$.

The corresponding latent column vectors can be identified as

$$\mathbf{h}_1 = \{1, \tfrac{4}{3}, 1\}, \quad \mathbf{h}_2 = \{1, 0, -1\}, \quad \mathbf{h}_3 = \{1, -2, 1\}.$$

[†] The latent column vectors and the reciprocal matrix H^{-1} are obtained by the standard methods described in *Determinants and Matrices* by A. C. Aitken and other books on matrix algebra.

Thus

$$H = \begin{bmatrix} 1 & 1 & 1 \\ \frac{4}{3} & 0 & -2 \\ 1 & -1 & 1 \end{bmatrix} \quad \text{and} \quad H^{-1} = \begin{bmatrix} \frac{3}{10} & \frac{3}{10} & \frac{3}{10} \\ \frac{1}{2} & 0 & -\frac{1}{2} \\ \frac{1}{5} & -\frac{3}{10} & \frac{1}{5} \end{bmatrix},$$

whence we obtain

$$[p_{ij}^{(n)}] = P^n = H\Lambda^n H^{-1} =$$

$$\begin{bmatrix} \frac{3}{10}\lambda_1^n + \frac{1}{2}\lambda_2^n + \frac{1}{5}\lambda_3^n & \frac{3}{10}\lambda_1^n - \frac{3}{10}\lambda_3^n & \frac{3}{10}\lambda_1^n - \frac{1}{2}\lambda_2^n + \frac{1}{5}\lambda_3^n \\ \frac{2}{5}\lambda_1^n - \frac{2}{5}\lambda_3^n & \frac{2}{5}\lambda_1^n + \frac{3}{5}\lambda_3^n & \frac{2}{5}\lambda_1^n - \frac{2}{5}\lambda_3^n \\ \frac{3}{10}\lambda_1^n - \frac{1}{2}\lambda_2^n + \frac{1}{5}\lambda_3^n & \frac{3}{10}\lambda_1^n - \frac{3}{10}\lambda_3^n & \frac{3}{10}\lambda_1^n + \frac{1}{2}\lambda_2^n + \frac{1}{5}\lambda_3^n \end{bmatrix}$$

$$\{p_i^{(n)}\} = P^n\{1, 0, 0\} = \begin{bmatrix} \frac{3}{10}\lambda_1^n + \frac{1}{2}\lambda_2^n + \frac{1}{5}\lambda_3^n \\ \frac{2}{5}\lambda_1^n - \frac{2}{5}\lambda_3^n \\ \frac{3}{10}\lambda_1^n - \frac{1}{2}\lambda_2^n + \frac{1}{5}\lambda_3^n \end{bmatrix}.$$

Since $\lambda_1 = 1$, $|\lambda_2| < 1$ and $|\lambda_3| < 1$, it follows that as $n \to \infty$

$$[p_{ij}^{(n)}] \to \begin{bmatrix} \frac{3}{10} & \frac{3}{10} & \frac{3}{10} \\ \frac{2}{5} & \frac{2}{5} & \frac{2}{5} \\ \frac{3}{10} & \frac{3}{10} & \frac{3}{10} \end{bmatrix} \quad \text{and} \quad \{p_i^{(n)}\} \to \begin{bmatrix} \frac{3}{10} \\ \frac{2}{5} \\ \frac{3}{10} \end{bmatrix}.$$

We observe that for each i, $p_{ij}^{(n)}$ tends to a limit which is independent of j. Thus it follows that the absolute probabilities $p_i^{(n)} = \sum_{j=1}^{3} p_{ij}^{(n)} p_j$ must also tend to this common limit (since $\sum_{j=1}^{3} p_j = 1$) and so we have the final result that the limiting behaviour of $\{p_i^{(n)}\}$ is independent of the initial probability distribution $\{p_j\}$ and hence of the initial state of the system.

§52. Properties of stochastic matrices.

(1) *Every stochastic matrix P has a latent root equal to* 1.

To prove this we observe that since $\sum_i p_{ij} = 1$ for all j it follows that

$$[1, 1, 1, \ldots\,] P = [\sum_i p_{i1}, \sum_i p_{i2}, \sum_i p_{i3}, \ldots]$$

$$= 1 \,.\, [1, 1, 1, \ldots .].$$

Thus 1 is a latent root, and $[1, 1, 1, \ldots]$ is the associated latent row vector.

(2) *If P is stochastic, so is P^n for any positive integer n.*

Since the elements p_{ij} of P are non-negative it follows that the elements of P^n, namely $p_{ij}^{(n)}$, are also $\geqslant 0$. The fact that the column totals are unity can be established by the consideration that $\sum_i p_{ij}^{(n)}$ represents the probability that if the system started in E_j then after the nth trial it is in some state; this is certain and hence must have probability 1.

Alternatively, we may use (1), for since 1 is a latent root of P with associated latent row vector $[1, 1, 1, \ldots]$ it follows from matrix theory that 1^n, and hence 1, is a latent root of P^n with latent row vector $[1, 1, 1, \ldots]$. Hence we have

$$[1, 1, 1, \ldots] P^n = [1, 1, 1, \ldots]$$

from which it follows that $\sum_i p_{ij}^{(n)} = 1$ for all j.

(3) *All latent roots λ of a stochastic matrix satisfy $|\lambda| \leqslant 1$.*

Since $P^n = H\Lambda^n H^{-1}$ it follows that $\Lambda^n = H^{-1} P^n H$.

Now the diagonal elements of Λ^n (even in the case of repeated latent roots) are λ_i^n and if any $|\lambda_i| > 1$ it would follow that as n increased the corresponding diagonal element of Λ^n would increase in magnitude without limit. But the ith diagonal element of Λ^n is given by

$$\sum_j \sum_k h_{ij}^* p_{jk}^{(n)} h_{ki}$$

where h_{ij}^* is the (i, j)th element of H^{-1} and h_{ki} is the (k, i)th element of H. Since all $p_{jk}^{(n)} \leqslant 1$, it follows that the modulus of the ith diagonal element of Λ^n cannot exceed $\sum_j \sum_k |h_{ij}^*| \cdot |h_{ki}|$ which is bounded. Hence the assumption that $|\lambda_i| > 1$ leads to a contradiction and so all latent roots must satisfy $|\lambda| \leqslant 1$.

It is thus seen that $\lambda = 1$ is the latent root of maximum modulus, but, of course, it can be a repeated root, and there may be other latent roots with $|\lambda| = 1$, that is $\lambda = -1$ or some complex value.

(4) Using matrix theory, A. C. Aitken has proved that a necessary and sufficient condition for $p_{ij}^{(n)}$ to tend to a limit independent of j, and hence for the limiting absolute probabilities to be independent of the initial condition of the system, is that $\lambda = 1$ is a non-repeated latent root of P and all other latent roots are strictly less than 1 in modulus. This condition was satisfied by the example in §51 where it was shown directly that the stated limiting properties held.

§53. Examples of Markov chains

(1) A counter starts at random from one square on a square board containing nine equal squares. At each move the counter is equally likely to move to any neighbour-

ing square in the horizontal, vertical or diagonal direction. It is required to examine the probabilities of the counter being in different squares after n moves.

E_1	E_2	E_1
E_2	E_3	E_2
E_1	E_2	E_1

At first sight it appears that the system has nine possible states and hence that the transition matrix must be of order 9×9. Using symmetry, however, it is possible to treat the problem as that of a system having three states E_1, E_2, and E_3 as shown in the diagram. The matrix of transition probabilities P is then seen to be

$$P = \begin{bmatrix} \cdot & \frac{2}{5} & \frac{1}{2} \\ \frac{2}{3} & \frac{2}{5} & \frac{1}{2} \\ \frac{1}{3} & \frac{1}{5} & \cdot \end{bmatrix},$$

with latent roots $\lambda = 1, \dfrac{-0\cdot6 \pm \sqrt{0\cdot0933}}{2}$, so that $\lambda = 1$ is strictly dominant. Hence P^n and the limiting values of $p_{ij}^{(n)}$ and $p_i^{(n)}$ can be obtained, the latter being found to be independent of the square on which the counter is originally placed.

The absolute probability of the counter being on a particular E_1 square is then clearly $\frac{1}{4}p_1^{(n)}$, on a particular E_2 square, $\frac{1}{4}p_2^{(n)}$, and of course on the only E_3 square $p_3^{(n)}$. This problem can also be solved by the method of difference equations, cf. §41.

(2) Associated with a series of independent Bernoulli trials is the "system" defined to be the number of consecutive successes obtained, and so, after each trial the system is in one of the states E_0, E_1, E_2, ... where E_i denotes the appearance of the ith consecutive success at the last trial, E_0 of course denoting the appearance of a failure at the last trial.

Thus at any trial there are only two transitions possible:

$E_k \rightarrow E_{k+1}$ with probability p so that $p_{k+1, k} = p$.

$E_k \rightarrow E_0$ with probability q so that $p_{0, k}$ $= q$.

All other p_{ij} are zero, and the matrix P is now infinite, $i, j = 0, 1, 2, 3, \ldots$. Hence we have P given as

$$\begin{bmatrix} q & q & q & \cdot & \cdot & \ldots \\ p & \cdot & \cdot & \cdot & \cdot & \ldots \\ \cdot & p & \cdot & \cdot & \cdot & \ldots \\ \cdot & \cdot & p & \cdot & \cdot & \ldots \\ \cdot & \cdot & \cdot & \cdot & \cdot & \ldots \\ \cdot & \cdot & \cdot & \cdot & \cdot & \ldots \\ \cdot & \cdot & \cdot & \cdot & \cdot & \cdot & \cdot \end{bmatrix}$$

We observe that in this example the initial state of the system must be E_0 and so we must have

$$\{p_i\} = \{1, 0, 0, \ldots\}.$$

(3) The problem of the one-dimensional random walk with absorbing barriers, or the gambler's ruin problem, is also capable of this type of formulation.

A particle starts at $x = a$ and in each time interval moves unit distance to the right with probability p or to the left with probability q. The particle remains permanently at $x = 0$ or $x = a+b$ if and when it reaches either of these positions. It is clear that we are concerned with a system having states E_0, E_1, ..., E_{a+b} where E_i means that particle is at $x = i$. The transition probabilities are,

$$p(E_i \rightarrow E_{i+1}) = p_{i+1,\,i} = p \quad \text{for} \quad 0 < i < a+b,$$
$$p(E_i \rightarrow E_{i-1}) = p_{i-1,\,i} = q \quad \text{for} \quad 0 < i < a+b,$$
$$p_{0,\,0} = 1, \quad p_{a+b,\,a+b} = 1,$$

and all other $p_{ij} = 0$.

The $(a+b+1) \times (a+b+1)$ stochastic matrix is therefore

$$P = \begin{bmatrix}
1 & q & \cdot & \cdot & \cdot \ldots \cdot & \cdot & \cdot \\
\cdot & \cdot & q & \cdot & \cdot \ldots \cdot & \cdot & \cdot \\
\cdot & p & \cdot & q & \cdot \ldots \cdot & \cdot & \cdot \\
\cdot & \cdot & p & \cdot & q \ldots \cdot & \cdot & \cdot \\
\cdots\cdots\cdots\cdots\cdots\cdots\cdots\cdots\cdots\cdots \\
\cdot\cdot\cdot\cdot\cdot\cdot\cdot\cdot\cdot\cdot\cdot\cdot\cdot\cdot\ldots\cdot & q & \cdot \\
\cdot\cdot\cdot\cdot\cdot\cdot\cdot\cdot\cdot\cdot\cdot\cdot\cdot\cdot\ldots p & \cdot & \cdot \\
\cdot\cdot\cdot\cdot\cdot\cdot\cdot\cdot\cdot\cdot\cdot\cdot\cdot\cdot\ldots\cdot & p & 1
\end{bmatrix}$$

and the initial probability vector is

$$\mathbf{p}_0 = \{\ldots 1 \ldots\}$$

where the unit is the $(a+1)$th element in the $(a+b+1)$ element vector. The behaviour of the process and its limiting probabilities can now be studied.

(4) A probabilistic model introduced to describe diffusion

State E_k

of gases is an interesting example of the matrix formulation of a Markov chain. The Ehrenfest diffusion model consists of $2R$ balls numbered respectively $1, 2, 3, \ldots, 2R$, being initially distributed at random between two containers with k in the first and $(2R-k)$ in the second. An operation of the system consists in selecting at random one of the integers $1, 2, 3, \ldots, 2R$ and transferring the ball with that number from the container which it is in to the other container. The system can be in $2R+1$ possible states E_0, $E_1, E_2, \ldots, E_{2R}$ where E_i denotes the state that there are i balls in the first container. The transition probabilities are given by

$$p(E_i \rightarrow E_{i+1}) = p_{i+1, i} = \frac{2R-i}{2R}, \quad 0 \leqslant i < 2R,$$

$$p(E_i \rightarrow E_{i-1}) = p_{i-1, i} = \frac{i}{2R}, \qquad 0 < i \leqslant 2R,$$

and all other $p_{ij} = 0$.

The matrix of transition probabilities is thus of order $(2R+1) \times (2R+1)$ and is

$$P = \begin{bmatrix} \cdot & \dfrac{1}{2R} & \cdot & \cdot \ldots\ldots & \cdot & \cdot & \cdot \\ \dfrac{2R}{2R} & \cdot & \dfrac{2}{2R} & \cdot \ldots\ldots & \cdot & \cdot & \cdot \\ \cdot & \dfrac{2R-1}{2R} & \cdot & \dfrac{3}{2R} \ldots\ldots & \cdot & \cdot & \cdot \\ \cdots & \cdots & \cdots & \cdots & \cdots & \cdots & \cdots \\ \cdot & \cdot & \cdot & \cdot \ldots\ldots & \dfrac{2}{2R} & \cdot & \dfrac{2R}{2R} \\ \cdot & \cdot & \cdot & \cdot \ldots\ldots & \cdot & \dfrac{1}{2R} & \cdot \end{bmatrix}$$

and the initial probability vector is

$$\mathbf{p}_0 = \{\ldots 1 \ldots\}$$

where the unit is the $(k+1)$th element of the $(2R+1)$ ele-

ment vector. We shall examine this example in greater
detail in the next section.

§54. **Ehrenfest probability model.** To examine $p_{ij}^{(n)}$ and $p_i^{(n)}$
for this model the first step is to obtain the latent roots and
latent column vectors of P. While it is possible to find the
$(2R+1)$ latent roots as the roots of the equation

$$\left| P - \lambda I \right| = 0,$$

by evaluating the determinant by a reduction process, there
still remains the difficulty of finding the associated latent
column vectors. A better method is to use a generating
function to find the elements of the latent column vector
associated with a latent root λ, and then from general considerations it is possible to identify the $(2R+1)$ values of λ.

Let $\mathbf{h} = \{1, h_1, h_2, \ldots, h_{2R}\}$ be the latent column vector
associated with the latent root λ. Then, of course,

$$(P - \lambda I)\mathbf{h} = \mathbf{0}$$

and writing these equations in full, it is seen that the elements of $\mathbf{h}$ must satisfy the equations

$$-\lambda + \frac{1}{2R}h_1 = 0$$

$$\frac{2R}{2R} - \lambda h_1 + \frac{2}{2R}h_2 = 0$$

$$\frac{2R-1}{2R}h_1 - \lambda h_2 + \frac{3}{2R}h_3 = 0$$

$$\cdots \cdots \cdots \cdots \cdots \cdots$$

$$\frac{2}{2R}h_{2R-2} - \lambda h_{2R-1} + \frac{2R}{2R}h_{2R} = 0$$

$$\frac{1}{2R}h_{2R-1} - \lambda h_{2R} = 0.$$

Define $H(s) = \sum\limits_{r=0}^{2R} h_r s^r$ to be the generating function for the elements of **h**, where h_0 has been taken as 1 for convenience. If we multiply the above $(2R+1)$ linear equations by $1, s, s^2, \ldots, s^{2R}$ respectively and sum them we obtain

$$-\lambda \sum_{r=0}^{2R} h_r s^r + \frac{1}{2R} \sum_{r=0}^{2R} r h_r s^{r-1} + \frac{1}{2R} \sum_{r=0}^{2R} (2R-r) h_r s^{r+1} = 0.$$

Now $\dfrac{dH(s)}{ds} = \sum\limits_{r=0}^{2R} r h_r s^{r-1}$ and so it follows that on substitution we obtain

$$(s-\lambda)H(s) + \frac{1}{2R}(1-s^2)\frac{dH(s)}{ds} = 0;$$

since the first element of **h** is unity, this equation has the solution

$$H(s) = (1-s)^{R(1-\lambda)}(1+s)^{R(1+\lambda)}.$$

Now $H(s)$ must be a polynomial of degree $2R$ in s and we observe that if $\lambda = \dfrac{j}{R}$ where $j = -R, -(R-1), -(R-2), \ldots, -1, 0, 1, \ldots, (R-1), R$ then the solution of the differential equation is a polynomial of this degree. It can be verified that these values of λ are the latent roots of the matrix P, and hence the latent column vector corresponding to $\lambda = \dfrac{j}{R}$ has elements generated by

$$(1-s)^{R-j}(1+s)^{R+j}.$$

We shall refer to this vector as $\mathbf{h}^j = \{1, h_1^j, h_2^j, \ldots, h_{2R}^j\}$, and so we have

$$P = H\Lambda H^{-1}$$

where $H = [\mathbf{h}^{-R}, \mathbf{h}^{-(R-1)}, \ldots, \mathbf{h}^R]$, and it remains to obtain the elements of H^{-1}.

Let the ith row of H^{-1} be $[l_0^i, l_1^i, \ldots, l_{2R}^i]$, where, for convenience, we number the rows as $i = -R, -(R-1), \ldots, 0, \ldots, (R-1), R$.

Then since $HH^{-1} = I$ it follows that

$$\sum_{i=-R}^{R} h_r^i l_j^i = \delta_{rj} = \begin{cases} 1 \text{ if } r = j \\ 0 \text{ if } r \neq j \end{cases} \quad r = 0, 1, 2, \ldots 2R.$$

Thus we have

$$\begin{aligned} s^j &= \sum_{r=0}^{2R} \delta_{rj} s^r \\ &= \sum_{r=0}^{2R} s^r \sum_{i=-R}^{R} h_r^i l_j^i \\ &= \sum_{i=-R}^{R} l_j^i \sum_{r=0}^{2R} h_r^i s^r \\ &= \sum_{i=-R}^{R} l_j^i (1-s)^{R-i} (1+s)^{R+i} \\ &= (1-s)^{2R} \sum_{v=0}^{2R} l_j^{v-R} \left(\frac{1+s}{1-s} \right)^v. \end{aligned}$$

Thus

$$\frac{s^j}{(1-s)^{2R}} = \sum_{v=0}^{2R} l_j^{v-R} \left(\frac{1+s}{1-s} \right)^v.$$

Let $z = \dfrac{1+s}{1-s}$, giving $s = -\dfrac{1-z}{1+z}$ and $1-s = \dfrac{2}{1+z}$; then we

obtain

$$\frac{(-1)^j}{2^{2R}} (1-z)^j (1+z)^{2R-j} = \sum_{v=0}^{2R} l_j^{v-R} z^v.$$

But, since $(1-z)^j(1+z)^{2R-j} = \sum_{v=0}^{2R} h_v^{R-j} z^v$, we have

$$l_j^{v-R} = \frac{(-1)^j}{2^{2R}} h_v^{R-j},$$

that is

$$l_j^k = \frac{(-1)^j}{2^{2R}} h_{k+R}^{R-j}$$

for $k = -R, \ldots, R, \quad j = 0, \ldots, 2R.$

Then, finally, we see that

$$p_{ab}^{(n)} = (a+1, b+1)\text{th element of } H\Lambda^n H^{-1}$$

$$= \frac{(-1)^b}{2^{2R}} \sum_{j=0}^{2R} h_a^{j-R} \left(\frac{j-R}{R}\right)^n h_j^{R-b}.$$

As $n \to \infty$, the only terms in the summation which do not tend to zero are those for $j = 0$ and $j = 2R$. Thus, as $n \to \infty$, we have

$$p_{ab}^{(n)} \to \frac{(-1)^b}{2^{2R}} \{h_a^{-R}(-1)^n h_0^{R-b} + h_a^R(+1)^n h_{2R}^{R-b}\}$$

which oscillates between two values according as n is odd or even.

§55. Limiting distributions.

A limiting distribution is said to exist whenever the n-stage transition probabilities $p_{ij}^{(n)}$ tend to limiting values π_i which are independent of j. The limiting values of these probabilities may be obtained by solving the set of linear equations

$$\sum_i \pi_i = 1$$

and

$$\pi_i = \sum_k p_{ik}\pi_k \text{ for all values of } i,$$

the latter equations being obtained by taking the limit as $n \to \infty$ of the equations

$$p_{ij}^{(n+1)} = \sum_k p_{ik}p_{kj}^{(n)}.$$

It has been stated in §52 that one formulation of the necessary and sufficient conditions for the existence of a limiting distribution is that the transition matrix P should have a non-repeated latent root 1 and all other latent roots should be less than 1 in modulus. Since the Ehrenfest model also has -1 as a latent root, we know that for this chain P^n does not tend to a limit as $n \to \infty$. In fact this chain is periodic (see §58) with period 2 and P^n oscillates between two limiting values according as n is odd or even. However the following modified model does have a limiting distribution.

Suppose that the states are as in the Ehrenfest model but that the transition probabilities are given by

$$p_{ii} = \alpha, \qquad 0 \leqslant i \leqslant 2R,$$

$$p_{i+1, i} = (1-\alpha)\frac{2R-i}{2R}, \qquad 0 \leqslant i < 2R,$$

$$p_{i-1, i} = (1-\alpha)\frac{i}{2R}, \qquad 0 < i \leqslant 2R,$$

where $0 < \alpha < 1$, all other p_{ij} being zero. This is equivalent to there being a positive probability α of the system not changing its state and $(1-\alpha)$ of changing. If a change of state occurs, then the conditional probabilities of the two possible changes are given by the Ehrenfest probabilities. It can be verified that the latent roots of P satisfy the necessary and sufficient conditions for the existence of a limiting distribution $\{\pi_i\}$ which must satisfy

$$\pi_0 = \alpha\pi_0 + \frac{(1-\alpha)}{2R}\pi_1,$$

$$\pi_1 = (1-\alpha)\frac{2R}{2R}\pi_0 + \alpha\pi_1 + (1-\alpha)\frac{2}{2R}\pi_2,$$

$$\pi_2 = (1-\alpha)\frac{2R-1}{2R}\pi_1 + \alpha\pi_2 + (1-\alpha)\frac{3}{2R}\pi_3,$$

$$\cdot \quad \cdot \quad \cdot \quad \cdot \quad \cdot \quad \cdot \quad \cdot \quad \cdot \quad \cdot \quad \cdot$$

$$\pi_{2R-1} = (1-\alpha)\frac{2}{2R}\pi_{2R-2} + \alpha\pi_{2R-1} + (1-\alpha)\frac{2R}{2R}\pi_{2R},$$

$$\pi_{2R} = (1-\alpha)\frac{1}{2R}\pi_{2R-1} + \alpha\pi_{2R}.$$

Multiplying these equations respectively by $1, s, s^2, \ldots, s^{2R}$ and adding, we obtain

$$\sum_{i=0}^{2R}\pi_i s^i = (1-\alpha)\sum_{i=0}^{2R}\frac{2R-i}{2R}\pi_i s^{i+1} + \alpha\sum_{i=0}^{2R}\pi_i s^i$$

$$+ (1-\alpha)\sum_{i=0}^{2R}\frac{i}{2R}\pi_i s^{i-1},$$

whence, defining $G(s) = \sum_{i=0}^{2R}\pi_i s^i$ to be the limiting probability generating function, it follows that

$$2RG(s) = (1-\alpha)2RsG(s) - (1-\alpha)s^2\frac{dG(s)}{ds}$$

$$+ 2\alpha RG(s) + (1-\alpha)\frac{dG(s)}{ds},$$

$$2R(1-\alpha)(1-s)G(s) = (1-\alpha)(1-s^2)\frac{dG(s)}{ds},$$

$$2RG(s) = (1+s)\frac{dG(s)}{ds}.$$

Solving this differential equation, we find

$$G(s) = k(1+s)^{2R}.$$

But $G(1) = \sum_{i=0}^{2R} \pi_i = 1$, and so $k = 1/2^{2R}$.

Thus

$$G(s) = \frac{(1+s)^{2R}}{2^{2R}},$$

and

$$\pi_i = \binom{2R}{i}\bigg/2^{2R}, \quad i = 0, 1, 2, \ldots, 2R.$$

From general matrix theory it is known that if P has a non-repeated latent root with modulus strictly greater than that of any other latent root, then for any arbitrary vector $\mathbf{v}$, as $n \to \infty$ the vector $P^n\mathbf{v}$ tends to a latent column vector corresponding to the maximum modulus latent root. Thus when a limiting distribution exists it must be given by the latent column vector corresponding to $\lambda = 1$ scaled so that the sum of its elements is unity.

We can see that the recurrence relations used in the above derivation of the values $\{\pi_i\}$ are in fact equivalent to

$$P\pi = \lambda\pi, \text{ with } \lambda = 1,$$

so that $\{\pi_i\}$ is given by the corresponding latent column vector scaled so that $\sum_i \pi_i = 1$.

§56. Stationary distributions. Even although a chain does not have a limiting distribution in the sense of the previous section, that is P^n does not tend to a limit as $n \to \infty$ and so $p_{ij}^{(n)}$ does not tend to π_i independent of j, it is seen that if the initial probability distribution satisfies the equation

$$P\mathbf{p} = \mathbf{p}$$

then the n-stage probability distribution $\mathbf{p}^{(n)}$ must also be $\mathbf{p}$. Hence the distribution given by the solution of the equations

$$p_i = \sum_j p_{ij} p_j$$

is such that if the condition of the system at any stage is governed by it, the system will continue to be governed by that distribution thereafter.

In the case of the basic Ehrenfest model these equations are

$$p_0 \quad = \quad \frac{1}{2R} p_1,$$

$$p_1 \quad = \frac{2R}{2R} p_0 \quad + \frac{2}{2R} p_2,$$

$$p_2 \quad = \frac{2R-1}{2R} p_1 \; + \frac{3}{2R} p_3,$$

$$\cdot \quad \cdot \quad \cdot \quad \cdot \quad \cdot \quad \cdot \quad \cdot \quad \cdot \quad \cdot \quad \cdot$$

$$p_{2R-1} = \frac{2}{2R} \, p_{2R-2} + \frac{2R}{2R} p_{2R},$$

$$p_{2R} \quad = \frac{1}{2R} \, p_{2R-1},$$

together with the condition $\sum_j p_j = 1$.

Multiplying these respectively by $1, s, s^2, \ldots, s^{2R}$ and summing we have

$$\sum_{j=0}^{2R} p_j s^j = \sum_{j=0}^{2R} \frac{2R-j}{2R} p_j s^{j+1} + \sum_{j=0}^{2R} \frac{j}{2R} p_j s^{j-1}$$

whence defining $G(s) = \sum_{j=0}^{2R} p_j s^j$ it follows that

$$2RG(s) = 2RsG(s) - s^2 \frac{dG(s)}{ds} + \frac{dG(s)}{ds},$$

$$2R(1-s)G(s) = (1-s^2)\frac{dG(s)}{ds},$$

$$2RG(s) = (1+s)\frac{dG(s)}{ds}.$$

Integrating and using the property $G(1) = \sum_{j=0}^{2R} p_j = 1$ we obtain

$$G(s) = \frac{(1+s)^{2R}}{2^{2R}}$$

and so

$$p_j = \binom{2R}{j} \bigg/ 2^{2R}.$$

Hence it is seen that the limiting distribution for the modified Ehrenfest model is also the stationary distribution for the basic model which does not have a limiting distribution.

§57. Limiting $p^{(n)}$ distributions when P^n does not tend to a limit. In cases when P^n does not tend to a limit, but oscillates between a number of limiting values—such a situation arises in the case of a periodic chain—it may be possible to find a family of initial probability distributions which ensure that $p^{(n)} \to \pi$. It is obvious that the stationary distribution must be included in any such family, and it is of interest to examine what other initial distributions lead to such a property.

Rather than attempt a general investigation of the problem, we illustrate the ideas by a simple example. Consider a four-state system with transition probabilities given by the matrix

$$P = \begin{bmatrix} \cdot & \frac{1}{3} & \cdot & \cdot \\ 1 & \cdot & \frac{2}{3} & \cdot \\ \cdot & \frac{2}{3} & \cdot & 1 \\ \cdot & \cdot & \frac{1}{3} & \cdot \end{bmatrix}$$

The four latent roots are $1, \frac{1}{3}, -\frac{1}{3}, -1$ and it is observed that the existence of the root -1 will result in there being no limiting value of P^n. In fact it is found that

$$P^n \to \begin{bmatrix} \cdot & \frac{1}{4} & \cdot & \frac{1}{4} \\ \frac{3}{4} & \cdot & \frac{3}{4} & \cdot \\ \cdot & \frac{3}{4} & \cdot & \frac{3}{4} \\ \frac{1}{4} & \cdot & \frac{1}{4} & \cdot \end{bmatrix} \text{ when } n \text{ is odd,}$$

and

$$P^n \to \begin{bmatrix} \frac{1}{4} & \cdot & \frac{1}{4} & \cdot \\ \cdot & \frac{3}{4} & \cdot & \frac{3}{4} \\ \frac{3}{4} & \cdot & \frac{3}{4} & \cdot \\ \cdot & \frac{1}{4} & \cdot & \frac{1}{4} \end{bmatrix} \text{ when } n \text{ is even.}$$

Now any initial distribution $\mathbf{p} = \{p_1, p_2, p_3, p_4\}$ which satisfies the relation

$$\begin{bmatrix} \cdot & \frac{1}{4} & \cdot & \frac{1}{4} \\ \frac{3}{4} & \cdot & \frac{3}{4} & \cdot \\ \cdot & \frac{3}{4} & \cdot & \frac{3}{4} \\ \frac{1}{4} & \cdot & \frac{1}{4} & \cdot \end{bmatrix} \begin{bmatrix} p_1 \\ p_2 \\ p_3 \\ p_4 \end{bmatrix} = \begin{bmatrix} \frac{1}{4} & \cdot & \frac{1}{4} & \cdot \\ \cdot & \frac{3}{4} & \cdot & \frac{3}{4} \\ \frac{3}{4} & \cdot & \frac{3}{4} & \cdot \\ \cdot & \frac{1}{4} & \cdot & \frac{1}{4} \end{bmatrix} \begin{bmatrix} p_1 \\ p_2 \\ p_3 \\ p_4 \end{bmatrix}$$

will ensure that $\mathbf{p}^{(n)} \to \pi$.

We see that the elements of $\mathbf{p}$ must satisfy

$$p_1 + p_3 = p_2 + p_4$$

and since $p_1 + p_2 + p_3 + p_4 = 1$, this means $p_1 + p_3 = p_2 + p_4 = \frac{1}{2}$ where $p_i \geqslant 0$.

For any such initial distribution, $\mathbf{p}^{(n)}$ has the limiting value $\{\frac{1}{8}, \frac{3}{8}, \frac{3}{8}, \frac{1}{8}\}$ for both odd and even values of n. In fact this distribution itself satisfies $p_1 + p_3 = p_2 + p_4 = \frac{1}{2}$ and could be taken as an initial distribution which resulted in a limiting $\mathbf{p}^{(n)}$. It can be verified that this is also the stationary distribution satisfying

$$P\{\tfrac{1}{8}, \tfrac{3}{8}, \tfrac{3}{8}, \tfrac{1}{8}\} = \{\tfrac{1}{8}, \tfrac{3}{8}, \tfrac{3}{8}, \tfrac{1}{8}\}.$$

Thus we have found that three types of limiting distribution may exist for Markov chains.

(1) Limiting distribution $\{\pi_i\}$ which exists whenever P^n tends to a limit such that $p_{ij}^{(n)} = \pi_i$ for all j and hence $\mathbf{p}^{(n)} \to \pi$.

(2) Stationary distribution $\{p_i\}$ which is given by the solution to the equation $P\{p_i\} = \{p_i\}$. This is seen to be the scaled latent column vector associated with the latent root $\lambda = 1$ which any stochastic matrix P is known to have. If the initial distribution is $\{p_i\}$ then $\{p_i^{(n)}\}$ is always equal to $\{p_i\}$.

(3) Pseudo-limiting distribution $\{\pi_i\}$ associated with periodic chains which is only reached from a particular family of initial distributions, including the stationary distribution, and this limiting distribution is the stationary distribution.

§58. Classification of states.

The Markov chain consisting of a physical system with states E_1, E_2, ... and constant transition probabilities is closely linked with the theory of recurrent events. In fact the initial state of the system satisfies all the requirements of a recurrent event. Other states subsequent to their first appearance behave as recurrent events. Consequently the limiting properties of recurrent event theory are applicable to Markov chains.

Suppose that the initial state of the system is E_j and let $f_j^{(n)}$ denote the probability that the system returns to E_j for the first time after n transitions. The probability that the system returns to E_j after n transitions, not necessarily for the first time, is defined to be $p_{jj}^{(n)}$ and we see that

$$p_{jj}^{(1)} = f_j^{(1)} = p_{jj},$$
$$p_{jj}^{(2)} = f_j^{(2)} + f_j^{(1)} p_{jj}^{(1)},$$
$$. \quad . \quad . \quad . \quad . \quad . \quad .$$
$$p_{jj}^{(n)} = f_j^{(n)} + f_j^{(n-1)} p_{jj}^{(1)} + f_j^{(n-2)} p_{jj}^{(2)} + \cdots + f_j^{(1)} p_{jj}^{(n-1)}.$$

From these equations, if the values of $p_{jj}^{(n)}$ are known, successive substitution gives the values of the $f_j^{(n)}$. Since E_j is a recurrent event, we observe that the results of Chapter VI apply with the change of notation that $\{f_n\}$ and $\{a_n\}$ are now given by $\{f_j^{(n)}\}$ and $\{p_{jj}^{(n)}\}$ respectively.

The probability that E_j ever recurs is $\sum_{n=1}^{\infty} f_j^{(n)}$ and following the recurrent event classification we say that E_j is

recurrent or **persistent** if $\sum\limits_{n=1}^{\infty} f_j^{(n)} = 1$, while if $\sum\limits_{n=1}^{\infty} f_j^{(n)} < 1$ then E_j is said to be **transient**. Furthermore, for recurrent states, the mean recurrence time $\tau_j = \sum\limits_{n=1}^{\infty} n f_j^{(n)}$ can be finite or infinite. When τ_j is finite, E_j is said to be **non-null**; when τ_j is infinite, E_j is said to be **null**.

All three classes of states, recurrent non-null, recurrent null and transient, are further subdivided according to their periodicity. As for recurrent events we describe a state E_j as having period α if a return to E_j is impossible except possibly after $\alpha, 2\alpha, 3\alpha, \ldots$ transitions and α is the largest integer satisfying this property. When $\alpha = 1$, E_j is said to be **aperiodic**. A recurrent non-null state which is aperiodic is said to be **ergodic**.

Applying the results of §§45 and 46 we have the following properties:

(i)　E_j is a transient state if $\sum\limits_{n=1}^{\infty} p_{jj}^{(n)}$ is convergent.

(ii)　E_j is a recurrent or persistent state if $\sum\limits_{n=1}^{\infty} p_{jj}^{(n)}$ is divergent.

(iii)　$p_{jj}^{(n)} \to \dfrac{1}{\tau_j}$ if E_j is ergodic.

(iv)　$p_{jj}^{(n)} \to 0$ if E_j is null.

(v)　$p_{jj}^{(n\alpha)} \to \dfrac{\alpha}{\tau_j}$ if E_j is recurrent non-null with period α.

§59. Reducible and irreducible chains. A set, C, of states of a Markov chain is said to be **closed** if no one-step transition is possible from any state belonging to C to any state outside C. Thus $p_{kj} = 0$ for any $E_j \in C$ and any $E_k \notin C$. This condition obviously implies that $p_{kj}^{(n)} = 0$ for

P O

all n, and so we see that once a system reaches a state belonging to C it can never subsequently be in any state outside C.

In the special case where C consists of the single state E_j, $p_{jj} = 1$ and E_j is described as an **absorbing state**.

A chain in which there are two or more closed sets is said to be **reducible**; the chain is called **irreducible** if there exists no closed set other than the set of all states.

In a reducible chain with $E_j \in C$ and $E_k \notin C$ since $p_{kj}^{(n)} = 0$ it follows that $\sum_v p_{vj}^{(n)} = 1$ where the summation with respect to v extends over all $E_v \in C$. Hence if all rows and columns which relate to states not contained in C are removed from P there will remain a matrix which is still stochastic. Hence the subchain consisting only of the states of C is itself a Markov chain whose properties can be separately examined. Such a chain is irreducible.

If E_j is a recurrent state and if E_k is any state which can be reached from it, then there must exist a minimum path length l for which $p_{kj}^{(l)} = \alpha > 0$. A return from E_k to E_j must always be possible since otherwise there would be a probability of at least α that E_j will not recur and this is impossible since E_j is recurrent. Hence there must be a minimum path length m for which $p_{jk}^{(m)} = \beta > 0$. It follows that for any positive integer n,

$$p_{jj}^{(l+m+n)} \geqslant p_{kj}^{(l)} p_{kk}^{(n)} p_{jk}^{(m)} = \alpha\beta p_{kk}^{(n)},$$
$$p_{kk}^{(l+m+n)} \geqslant p_{jk}^{(m)} p_{jj}^{(n)} p_{kj}^{(l)} = \alpha\beta p_{jj}^{(n)}.$$

These two inequalities show that as $n \to \infty$, $p_{jj}^{(n)}$ and $p_{kk}^{(n)}$ must asymptotically behave in the same way. In particular, since E_j is recurrent, $\sum_{n=1}^{\infty} p_{jj}^{(n)}$ diverges and so $\sum_{n=1}^{\infty} p_{kk}^{(n)}$ diverges, which means that E_k is recurrent. If $p_{jj}^{(n)} \to 0$ so must

$p_{kk}^{(n)} \to 0$ which establishes that E_k is recurrent null if and only if E_j is recurrent null. Furthermore it is clear that E_j and E_k must have the same periodicity.

Since the set of all states which can be reached from E_j is a closed set (the smallest set containing E_j) it follows that in an irreducible chain every state can be reached from every other state and hence if one state is transient, so necessarily are all the others.

From these results the following theorem can be stated.

In an irreducible Markov chain all states belong to the same class. They must be all transient, all recurrent null or all recurrent non-null, and in every case have the same periodicity.

§60. Limiting properties of $p_{jk}^{(n)}$.

If $f_{jk}^{(n)}$ denotes the probability that a system initially in state E_k is found to be in state E_j for the first time after n transitions, then

$$p_{jk}^{(n)} = f_{jk}^{(n)} + f_{jk}^{(n-1)} p_{jj}^{(1)} + f_{jk}^{(n-2)} p_{jj}^{(2)} + \cdots + f_{jk}^{(1)} p_{jj}^{(n-1)}.$$

From this, provided the sequence of probabilities $\{p_{jj}^{(n)}\}$ is known, it is possible to express either of the sequences $\{p_{jk}^{(n)}\}$ or $\{f_{jk}^{(n)}\}$ in terms of the other. Also from this equation it is possible to establish two theorems relating to the limiting behaviour of $p_{jk}^{(n)}$.

THEOREM 1. *If E_j is either transient or recurrent null, then for any periodicity as $n \to \infty$, $p_{jk}^{(n)} \to 0$ for any value of k.*

From §58 it is seen that $p_{jj}^{(n)} \to 0$ and so for every fixed N it follows that the last N terms on the right-hand side of the equation for $p_{jk}^{(n)}$ tend to zero. The sum of the remaining $(n-N)$ terms add to not more than $f_{jk}^{(n)} + f_{jk}^{(n-1)} + \cdots + f_{jk}^{(N+1)}$ since $p_{jj}^{(r)} \leqslant 1$; since $\sum\limits_{n=1}^{\infty} f_{jk}^{(n)}$ is convergent, being

$\leqslant 1$, it follows that the sum of the first $(n-N)$ terms on the right-hand side can be made arbitrarily small by choosing N large enough. Thus $p_{jk}^{(n)} \to 0$.

THEOREM 2. *If the states of an irreducible chain are all ergodic, then for every j, k as $n \to \infty$, $p_{jk}^{(n)} \to \dfrac{1}{\tau_j} > 0$ where τ_j is the mean recurrence time of E_j.*

From §58, $p_{jj}^{(n)} \to \dfrac{1}{\tau_j}$ and since E_j is recurrent, $\sum\limits_{n=1}^{\infty} f_{jk}^{(n)} = 1$ for any k. Thus for $\varepsilon > 0$ there exists an integer N such that

$$f_{jk}^{(1)} + f_{jk}^{(2)} + \ldots + f_{jk}^{(N)} > 1 - \varepsilon.$$

The last N terms of the expression for $p_{jk}^{(n)}$ are thus seen, as $n \to \infty$, to differ arbitrarily little from $\dfrac{1}{\tau_j}(f_{jk}^{(1)} + f_{jk}^{(2)} + \ldots + f_{jk}^{(N)})$, that is from $\dfrac{1}{\tau_j}$. The sum of the first $(n-N)$ terms again is less than the Nth remainder of the convergent series $\sum\limits_{n=1}^{\infty} f_{jk}^{(n)}$ and so can be made arbitrarily small. Thus $p_{jk}^{(n)} \to \dfrac{1}{\tau_j}$ for all k.

EXERCISES VII

1. Show that the three state Markov chain with transition matrix

$$P = \begin{bmatrix} \cdot & \tfrac{1}{2} & \cdot \\ 1 & \cdot & 1 \\ \cdot & \tfrac{1}{2} & \cdot \end{bmatrix}$$

is periodic with period 2. Examine the behaviour of P^n as $n \to \infty$ and find for what initial probability distributions the n-stage distribution $\{p_j^{(n)}\}$ tends to the stationary distribution.

Prove that the modified chain for which

$$P = \begin{bmatrix} \alpha & \tfrac{1}{2}(1-\alpha) & \cdot \\ (1-\alpha) & \alpha & (1-\alpha) \\ \cdot & \tfrac{1}{2}(1-\alpha) & \alpha \end{bmatrix} \quad 0 < \alpha < 1,$$

has a limiting distribution $\{p_j^{(n)}\}$ for any initial distribution.

2. The transition probability matrix for a four-state random walk with reflecting barriers is

$$\begin{bmatrix} \tfrac{2}{3} & \tfrac{2}{3} & \cdot & \cdot \\ \tfrac{1}{3} & \cdot & \tfrac{2}{3} & \cdot \\ \cdot & \tfrac{1}{3} & \cdot & \tfrac{2}{3} \\ \cdot & \cdot & \tfrac{1}{3} & \tfrac{1}{3} \end{bmatrix}.$$

Find the n-stage transition probability matrix and hence obtain the limiting probability distribution for the system as $n \to \infty$. Show that this distribution is independent of the initial distribution and find the mean recurrence times of the four states.

3. A four-state Markov chain has transition matrix given by

$$\begin{bmatrix} \frac{1}{2} & \frac{1}{6} & \cdot & \cdot \\ \frac{1}{2} & \frac{1}{2} & \frac{1}{3} & \cdot \\ \cdot & \frac{1}{3} & \frac{1}{2} & \frac{1}{2} \\ \cdot & \cdot & \frac{1}{6} & \frac{1}{2} \end{bmatrix}$$

Find the matrix of n-stage transition probabilities and hence show that the n-stage absolute probabilities tend to limits independent of the initial distribution.

Find the probabilities of the system being in the first state after three transitions for the following initial distributions:

(i) $\{1, 0, 0, 0\}$; (ii) $\{0, 0, 0, 1\}$; (iii) $\{\frac{1}{4}, \frac{1}{4}, \frac{1}{4}, \frac{1}{4}\}$;
(iv) $\{\frac{1}{8}, \frac{3}{8}, \frac{3}{8}, \frac{1}{8}\}$.

4. A three-state Markov chain has transition probability matrix

$$\begin{bmatrix} p & \frac{1}{2}q & \cdot \\ q & p & q \\ \cdot & \frac{1}{2}q & p \end{bmatrix}$$

where $0 \leqslant p \leqslant 1$ and $q = 1-p$.

Find the matrix of n-stage transition probabilities and hence show that for $0 < p < 1$ the n-stage absolute probabilities tend to limits independent of the initial distribution. What are the mean recurrence times of the states in this limiting distribution?

Examine the limiting behaviour of the chain (i) for $p = 0$ and (ii) for $p = 1$. In each case identify the stationary distribution and find for what other initial distribution the n-stage absolute probabilities tend to limits as $n \to \infty$.

5. The transition probability matrix for a cyclical four-state random walk is

$$\begin{bmatrix} \cdot & q & \cdot & p \\ p & \cdot & q & \cdot \\ \cdot & p & \cdot & q \\ q & \cdot & p & \cdot \end{bmatrix}$$

where $0 < p < 1$, $q = 1 - p$ and $p \neq q$.

Find the matrix of n-stage transition probabilities and hence show that

$$p_{kj}^{(n)} = \tfrac{1}{4}\{1 + (p-q)^n i^{j-k+n}\}\{1 + (-1)^{j+k+n}\}$$

where $i = \sqrt{-1}$.

Examine the behaviour of $[p_{kj}^{(n)}]$ as $n \to \infty$ and discuss the probability distribution after n transitions when the initial distribution is given by

(i) $\{1, 0, 0, 0\}$; (ii) $\{\tfrac{1}{6}, \tfrac{1}{3}, \tfrac{1}{3}, \tfrac{1}{6}\}$; (iii) $\{\tfrac{1}{4}, \tfrac{1}{4}, \tfrac{1}{4}, \tfrac{1}{4}\}$.

6. Show, by induction or otherwise, that the n-stage transition probabilities $p_{ij}^{(n)}$ for the four-state Markov chain with transition probability matrix

$$P = \begin{bmatrix} \cdot & \tfrac{1}{2} & \cdot & \cdot \\ 1 & \cdot & \tfrac{1}{2} & \cdot \\ \cdot & \tfrac{1}{2} & \cdot & 1 \\ \cdot & \cdot & \tfrac{1}{2} & \cdot \end{bmatrix}$$

are given by the elements of the matrix

$$\begin{bmatrix} 1 + u + 2v + 2w & 1 - u + v - w & 1 + u - v - w & 1 - u - 2v + 2w \\ 2 - 2u + 2v - 2w & 2 + 2u + v + w & 2 - 2u - v + w & 2 + 2u - 2v - 2w \\ 2 + 2u - 2v - 2w & 2 - 2u - v + w & 2 + 2u + v + w & 2 - 2u + 2v - 2w \\ 1 - u - 2v + 2w & 1 + u - v - w & 1 - u + v - w & 1 + u + 2v + 2w \end{bmatrix}$$

where $u = (-1)^n$, $v = (\tfrac{1}{2})^n$, $w = (-\tfrac{1}{2})^n$.

Obtain the stationary distribution and find for what other initial distributions the n-stage absolute probability distribution $\{p_j^{(n)}\}$ tends to a limiting distribution.

7. A Markov chain with three states has transition matrix

$$\begin{bmatrix} 1-p & p & \cdot \\ \cdot & 1-p & p \\ p & \cdot & 1-p \end{bmatrix}.$$

Show that $0 < p < 1$ is a necessary and sufficient condition for the existence of a limiting distribution of n-step transition probabilities as n tends to infinity, and find the limiting values of these probabilities.

Investigate the limiting behaviour of this chain when (i) $p = 0$ and (ii) $p = 1$.

Classify the states of the chain when (i) $p = 0$, (ii) $p = 1$ and (iii) $0 < p < 1$.

8. Find the matrix of n-stage transition probabilities for the five-state Markov chain with transition probabilities

$$P = \begin{bmatrix} \frac{1}{2} & \cdot & \cdot & \cdot & \cdot \\ \frac{1}{4} & \cdot & \cdot & \cdot & 1 \\ \cdot & 1 & \cdot & \cdot & \cdot \\ \frac{1}{4} & \cdot & 1 & \cdot & \cdot \\ \cdot & \cdot & \cdot & 1 & \cdot \end{bmatrix}$$

and discuss the behaviour of the system as $n \to \infty$.

Obtain the associated stationary distribution, and examine whether any other limiting distributions exist.

9. Ten coins lie on a table. The number, h, of coins with heads uppermost describes the state of the system. At each trial of the system one of the ten coins is selected at

random and turned over. Find the transition matrix and verify that the stationary distribution $\{\pi_h\}$ is given by

$$\pi_h = \binom{10}{h}\frac{1}{2^{10}}, \qquad h = 0, 1, 2, \ldots, 10.$$

10. Classify the states E_1, E_2, E_3, E_4 of the Markov chain which has the transition matrix

$$\begin{bmatrix} \cdot & \frac{1}{3} & \cdot & \frac{1}{6} \\ \frac{1}{3} & \cdot & \frac{1}{6} & \cdot \\ \cdot & \frac{2}{3} & \cdot & \frac{5}{6} \\ \frac{2}{3} & \cdot & \frac{5}{6} & \cdot \end{bmatrix}$$

If the system starts in state 1, how many steps must be made before the probability that the system has returned to state 1 exceeds 0·5?

CHAPTER VIII

MARKOV PROCESSES AND QUEUES

§61. Stochastic processes. In previous sections the behaviour of a discrete variate x was examined at a set of discrete points of "time", e.g., after $1, 2, 3, \ldots, n, \ldots$ transitions, and the resulting family of discrete probability distributions $\{p_x^{(n)}\}$ provided the complete description of the probable behaviour of x at all "times". In many of the examples, x denoted the state of some physical system and when $\{p_x^{(n)}\}$ is known for all values of n the future behaviour of the system is known in the probability sense. These were special cases of stochastic processes.

A **univariate stochastic process** is concerned with a variate x, which may be discrete or continuous, and its probability functions at all times t, where t can now range over all values in a continuous interval. The process is said to be completely determined when the joint probability distribution of $x(t_1), \ldots, x(t_n)$ is known for any set of n possible values of t, where $x(t_i)$ denotes the value taken by x at time t_i and where n can be any positive integer.

The mathematical treatment of processes for which both x and t are continuous is difficult and will not be developed in this book. However there are many practical situations with properties which can be described by a stochastic process with x discrete and t continuous. This chapter will be concerned with such processes.

To begin with, attention will be restricted to Markov processes which are analagous for continuous time to the discrete time Markov chains. This means that there is Markov type dependence between the behaviour of $x(t)$ at different times t in the sense that the behaviour of $x(t+\delta t)$ depends on the value taken by $x(t)$ but on no other earlier values of x.

§62. Poisson process.

The simplest Markov process is the Poisson process in which $x(t)$ denotes the total number of occurrences of some specified event in the time interval $(0, t)$ where individual occurrences are governed by the following rules.

(i)   Events happen independently of one another.

(ii) The probability that one event happens in the time interval $(t, t+\delta t)$ is $\lambda\delta t+o(\delta t)$ where λ is constant, and $o(\delta t)$ denotes terms of smaller order of magnitude than δt.

(iii) The probability that more than one event happens in the time interval $(t, t+\delta t)$ is $o(\delta t)$.

If $P_x(t)$ denotes the probability that x events happen in $(0, t)$, then by considering the time interval $(0, t+\delta t)$ as split into $(0, t)$ and $(t, t+\delta t)$ it follows that for $x \geqslant 1$,

$$P_x(t+\delta t) = P_x(t) \times \text{probability of no event in } (t, t+\delta t)$$

$$+ P_{x-1}(t) \times \text{probability of one event in } (t, t+\delta t)$$

$$+ \sum_{r=2}^{x} P_{x-r}(t) \times \text{probability of } r \text{ events in } (t, t+\delta t),$$

$$P_x(t+\delta t) = P_x(t) \times (1-\lambda\delta t-o(\delta t))$$
$$+ P_{x-1}(t) \times (\lambda\delta t+o(\delta t))+o(\delta t),$$

$$\frac{P_x(t+\delta t)-P_x(t)}{\delta t} = -\lambda P_x(t)+\lambda P_{x-1}(t)+\frac{o(\delta t)}{\delta t}.$$

If the limit as $\delta t \to 0$ is now taken, then since $\frac{o(\delta t)}{\delta t} \to 0$, we obtain

$$P'_x(t) = -\lambda P_x(t)+\lambda P_{x-1}(t),$$

where $P'_x(t)$ denotes $\frac{d}{dt}P_x(t)$.

For $x = 0$, by similar reasoning it is found that

$$P'_0(t) = -\lambda P_0(t).$$

Thus the behaviour of x is completely described by the system of equations

$$P'_0(t) = -\lambda P_0(t),$$

$$P'_x(t) = -\lambda P_x(t)+\lambda P_{x-1}(t), \quad x \geqslant 1,$$

together with the initial conditions that $P_0(0) = 1$, $P_x(0) = 0$ for $x \geqslant 1$.

Integrating the equation for $P_0(t)$ and using the condition $P_0(0) = 1$ it follows that

$$P_0(t) = e^{-\lambda t}.$$

Taking $x = 1$, substituting the value obtained for $P_0(t)$, integrating the resulting equation for $P_1(t)$ and using the initial condition $P_1(0) = 0$ we find that

$$P_1(t) = \lambda t e^{-\lambda t}.$$

Thereafter it can be successively established that

$$P_2(t) = \frac{(\lambda t)^2}{2!} e^{-\lambda t},$$

$$P_3(t) = \frac{(\lambda t)^3}{3!} e^{-\lambda t},$$

$$P_4(t) = \frac{(\lambda t)^4}{4!} e^{-\lambda t},$$

and so on, and finally, using induction it can be proved that

$$P_x(t) = \frac{(\lambda t)^x}{x!} e^{-\lambda t}, \quad x = 0, 1, 2, \ldots .$$

Thus the number of times the event governed by the probability rules (i), (ii) and (iii) will happen in the interval $(0, t)$, $x(t)$, has the discrete Poisson probability function $P_x(t)$ and for this reason the process is called the Poisson process.

It is instructive to consider an alternative method of solving the established set of differential equations for $P_x(t)$. If the associated probability generating function $G(s, t)$ is defined by

$$G(s, t) = \sum_{x=0}^{\infty} P_x(t) s^x,$$

then if the equation for $P_0'(t)$, s times the equation for $P_1'(t)$, s^2 times the equation for $P_2'(t), \ldots$ are added together, it is seen that the probability generating function must satisfy the differential equation

$$\frac{dG}{dt} = \lambda(s-1)G$$

since $\sum_{x=0}^{\infty} P_x'(t) s^x = \frac{dG}{dt}$ and $\sum_{x=1}^{\infty} s^x P_{x-1}(t) = s \sum_{x=0}^{\infty} s^x P_x(t) = sG$.

The initial conditions $P_0(0) = 1$, $P_x(0) = 0$ when $x \geqslant 1$

require that $G(s, 0) = 1$. Integrating the equation for G and using this condition we obtain

$$G(s, t) = e^{\lambda(s-1)t},$$

whence $P_x(t)$, being the coefficient of s^x in $G(s, t)$, is again found to be $e^{-\lambda t}\dfrac{(\lambda t)^x}{x!}$.

An associated feature of interest for the Poisson process is the probability function for the length of time which elapses before the event happens for the first time. The probability that the first occurrence is in the time interval $(t, t+\delta t)$ must be the product of the probability that the event has not happened in $(0, t)$, that is $P_0(t) = e^{-\lambda t}$, and the probability that the event happens in $(t, t+\delta t)$, that is $\lambda\delta t + o(\delta t)$. If we now divide this probability by δt and take the limit as $\delta t \to 0$, we obtain the continuous probability density function for the time t which elapses before the first occurrence of the event. Thus we have the continuous probability function given by

$$\underset{\delta t \to 0}{Lt}\ \frac{e^{-\lambda t}(\lambda\delta t + o(\delta t))}{\delta t} = \lambda e^{-\lambda t}, \quad 0 \leqslant t < \infty.$$

This is the negative exponential distribution defined in §25 and it is easily seen that the time elapsing between any two occurrences of the event must also have this probability function.

The pattern of occurrences of events in a Poisson process is described as being of random type with density λ. Such a model has been found useful in describing incoming calls in a telephone exchange, the arrival of customers requiring service in a shop and other practical situations. Some of these applications will be examined in later sections dealing with queues.

§63. Pure birth process. A generalisation of the Poisson process which still preserves the Markov dependence property is the pure birth process. Here the system consists of a population which cannot be depleted by "deaths" and which is subject to additions according to the following rules:

(i) The conditional probability that there is a single member added to the population in $(t,\ t+\delta t)$ when there are x members in the population at time t is $\lambda_x \delta t + o(\delta t)$ where λ_x depends on x.

(ii) The conditional probability of more than one addition to the population in $(t,\ t+\delta t)$ is always $o(\delta t)$.

Denoting the probability of a population of size x at time t by $P_x(t)$, then by the same type of argument as used for the Poisson process it follows that the following differential-difference equations must hold:

$$P_0'(t) = -\lambda_0 P_0(t)$$
$$P_x'(t) = -\lambda_x P_x(t) + \lambda_{x-1} P_{x-1}(t), \qquad x \geqslant 1.$$

To examine the properties of a particular process the function λ_x must be defined and the initial population size known. A case of practical interest is the linear pure birth process for which $\lambda_x = x\lambda$ where λ is constant. This arises when all existing members of the population act independently and have individual probability $\lambda \delta t + o(\delta t)$ of producing one additional member in $(t,\ t+\delta t)$. In such a process the initial population must be > 0, otherwise no population could ever exist. For simplicity it will be assumed that the initial population is unity so that $P_1(0) = 1$, and $P_x(0) = 0$ when $x > 1$.

As in the case of the Poisson process, when we substitute this value for λ_x and use these initial conditions, step by step integration of the recurrence equations is possible and leads to

$$P_0(t) = 0,$$
$$P_x(t) = e^{-\lambda t}(1-e^{-\lambda t})^{x-1}, \quad x \geqslant 1,$$

which can be proved by induction.

Again, however, by introducing the associated probability generating function $G(s, t) = \sum_{x=0}^{\infty} P_x(t)s^x$ it is possible to derive a differential equation for $G(s, t)$ which can be directly integrated. In this case a first order partial differential equation is obtained. Substituting $\lambda_x = x\lambda$,

$$P_0'(t) = 0,$$
$$P_1'(t) = -\lambda P_1(t),$$
$$P_2'(t) = -2\lambda P_2(t) + \lambda P_1(t),$$
$$P_3'(t) = -3\lambda P_3(t) + 2\lambda P_2(t),$$

. . . .

and multiplying these equations by 1, s, s^2, s^3, . . . respectively and adding, we find that

$$\frac{\partial G}{\partial t} = -\lambda s \frac{\partial G}{\partial s} + \lambda s^2 \frac{\partial G}{\partial s},$$

since $\dfrac{\partial G}{\partial t} = \sum_{x=0}^{\infty} P_x'(t)s^x$ and $\dfrac{\partial G}{\partial s} = \sum_{x=0}^{\infty} xP_x(t)s^{x-1}$.

To solve this partial differential equation it is first necessary to find two independent solutions of the system of ordinary differential equations

$$\frac{dt}{1} = \frac{ds}{-\lambda s(s-1)} = \frac{dG}{0}.$$

One solution is

$$G = \text{constant},$$

and from

$$\lambda\frac{dt}{1} = \frac{ds}{s} - \frac{ds}{s-1}$$

the second solution can be expressed in the form

$$\left(1 - \frac{1}{s}\right)e^{\lambda t} = \text{constant}.$$

The general solution of the partial differential equation can then be expressed in the form

$$G(s, t) = f\left\{\left(1 - \frac{1}{s}\right)e^{\lambda t}\right\},$$

and the particular solution which satisfies the initial conditions is obtained by using these conditions to determine the form of the function f.

The conditions $P_1(0) = 1$ and $P_x(0) = 0$ for $x > 1$ give $G(s, 0) = s$, and so putting $t = 0$ in the general solution and using this we have

$$s = f\left(1 - \frac{1}{s}\right).$$

Now let $u = 1 - \frac{1}{s}$, whence $s = \frac{1}{1-u}$, and it follows that

$$\frac{1}{1-u} = f(u)$$

which defines the function f.

P P

Thus finally

$$G(s, t) = \cfrac{1}{1-\left(1-\cfrac{1}{s}\right)e^{\lambda t}} = \frac{se^{-\lambda t}}{1-(1-e^{-\lambda t})s}$$

from which the values of $P_x(t)$ are obtained, by identifying the coefficients of s^x, as

$$P_0(t) = 0,$$

$$P_x(t) = e^{-\lambda t}(1-e^{-\lambda t})^{x-1}, \qquad x \geqslant 1.$$

These agree with the values established by the repeated integration and induction method.

This linear case of the pure birth process is known as the Yule-Furry process.

§64. Pure death process.

In the pure death process the state of the system, x, again denotes the size of a population. In this case, no additions to the population are ever possible; the population size is depleted by deaths governed by the following rules:

(i) The conditional probability that there is a single death in the population during the time interval $(t, t+\delta t)$ when there are x members in the population at time t is $\mu_x\delta t + o(\delta t)$ where μ_x depends on x.

(ii) The conditional probability of more than one death in $(t, t+\delta t)$ is always $o(\delta t)$.

If $P_x(t)$ denotes the probability of a population of size x at time t, it follows that

$$P_x'(t) = -\mu_x P_x(t) + \mu_{x+1}P_{x+1}(t), \qquad x \geqslant 0.$$

As in the case of the pure birth process, the basic case to be considered is the linear case for which $\mu_x = x\mu$ where μ is a constant. This arises when each member acts independently and has probability $\mu\delta t + o(\delta t)$ of dying in $(t, t+\delta t)$ if alive at time t. It is clear that the initial population must be greater than zero; suppose it to be n. Then the initial conditions are $P_n(0) = 1$ and $P_x(0) = 0$ for $x \neq n$.

Introducing again the generating function $G(s, t) = \sum_{x=0}^{\infty} P_x(t)s^x$, by multiplying the recurrence equation by s^x and summing over the values $x = 0, 1, 2, \ldots$, we obtain the partial differential equation,

$$\frac{\partial G}{\partial t} + \mu(s-1)\frac{\partial G}{\partial s} = 0,$$

for G. Solving this by the standard method used in §63 we find that

$$G(s, t) = \{(s-1)e^{-\mu t} + 1\}^n.$$

The probability $P_x(t)$ is given by the coefficient of s^x in this expansion. Now $G(s, t)$ can be written as $e^{-\mu n t}\{s + e^{\mu t} - 1\}^n$ and expanding this by the binomial theorem we obtain

$$P_x(t) = \binom{n}{x}e^{-\mu n t}(e^{\mu t}-1)^{n-x}, \quad x = 0, 1, 2, \ldots, n.$$

The probability of extinction of the population by time t is given by

$$P_0(t) = e^{-\mu n t}(e^{\mu t}-1)^n = (1-e^{-\mu t})^n$$

and, as would be expected, it is seen that this tends to 1 as t tends to infinity.

Another property of interest is the average time taken until the population becomes extinct. One method of evaluating this is to regard the total time T until extinction as being the sum of the times $t_1, t_2, \ldots, t_n$ where t_1 denotes the time until the first death occurs, t_2 denotes the time between the first and second deaths, $\ldots$, t_n denotes the time between the $(n-1)$th and nth deaths. The average value of T must clearly be given by the sum of the average values of $t_1, t_2, \ldots, t_n$. At a time when there are k members in the population it will be seen that the probability of a death in any instant δt is $k\mu\delta t + o(\delta t)$. By comparison with the results established in §62 it follows that the average time which will elapse before the first death occurs subsequent to this population of size k being reached is given by the arithmetic mean of the negative exponential distribution with probability function,

$$k\mu e^{-k\mu t}, \qquad 0 \leqslant t \leqslant \infty,$$

and this is found to be $\dfrac{1}{k\mu}$. Thus the average value of t_{n-k+1} is $\dfrac{1}{k\mu}$, and so the average value of T is

$$\sum_{k=1}^{n} \frac{1}{k\mu} = \frac{1}{\mu}\left\{1 + \frac{1}{2} + \frac{1}{3} + \ldots + \frac{1}{n}\right\}.$$

The alternative method of obtaining this property consists of observing that for the population to become extinct in $(t, t+\delta t)$ there must have been exactly one member living at time t and that member must die in $(t, t+\delta t)$. The joint probability of this is $P_1(t)\{\mu\delta t + o(\delta t)\}$ from which it follows that the total time to extinction has continuous probability function

$$\mu P_1(t) = n\mu e^{-n\mu t}(e^{\mu t}-1)^{n-1}, \qquad 0 \leqslant t \leqslant \infty,$$

and hence the mean time until extinction is

$$\int_0^\infty n\mu t e^{-n\mu t}(e^{\mu t}-1)^{n-1}dt,$$

which can be shown to agree with the value obtained above.

§65. **Polya process.** In the processes already considered, the conditional probabilities of a change in the state of the system at time $(t, t+\delta t)$ were all independent of time. The Polya process is a pure birth process for which the conditional probabilities of additions to the population are time-dependent and in consequence it is described as a non-homogeneous pure birth process. The conditional probability of a birth in $(t, t+\delta t)$ when there are x members in the population at time t is $\lambda \dfrac{1+\alpha x}{1+\alpha\lambda t}\delta t+o(\delta t)$, where λ and α are positive constants. As before, the probability of more than one birth in $(t, t+\delta t)$ is $o(\delta t)$ and no other changes can take place in the population.

Following the usual method, we find that the Polya process satisfies the difference-differential equations

$$P_0'(t) = -\frac{\lambda}{1+\alpha\lambda t}P_0(t),$$

$$P_x'(t) = \lambda\frac{1+\alpha(x-1)}{1+\alpha\lambda t}P_{x-1}(t)-\lambda\frac{1+\alpha x}{1+\alpha\lambda t}P_x(t), \qquad x \geqslant 1.$$

Introducing the generating function $G(s, t) = \sum\limits_{x=0}^\infty P_x(t)s^x$, multiplying the general recurrence equation by s^x and summing over $x = 1, 2, 3, \ldots$ and adding in the first differential equation for $P_0(t)$ we find that

$$(1 + \alpha\lambda t)\frac{\partial G}{\partial t} - \lambda\alpha s(s-1)\frac{\partial G}{\partial s} = \lambda(s-1)G.$$

To solve this it is necessary to find two independent solutions of the system of ordinary differential equations

$$\frac{dt}{1 + \alpha\lambda t} = \frac{-ds}{\lambda\alpha s(s-1)} = \frac{dG}{\lambda(s-1)G}.$$

From the equality between the first two expressions,

$$\frac{\alpha\lambda dt}{1 + \alpha\lambda t} = \frac{ds}{s} - \frac{ds}{s-1},$$

which on integrating gives

$$\frac{s-1}{s}(1 + \alpha\lambda t) = \text{constant}.$$

The equality between the last two expressions leads to

$$-\frac{ds}{s} = \frac{\alpha dG}{G},$$

with the solution

$$G^\alpha s = \text{constant}.$$

Hence the general solution of the partial differential equation is

$$G^\alpha s = f\left\{\frac{(s-1)(1 + \alpha\lambda t)}{s}\right\}$$

where the form of the function f must be determined by using the initial conditions of the process.

Suppose that initially there were no members in the population; then $P_0(0) = 1$ and $P_x(0) = 0$ for $x \geqslant 1$, and hence $G(s, 0) = 1$. Using this it follows that

$$s = f\left(\frac{s-1}{s}\right).$$

Now taking $u = \dfrac{s-1}{s}$ we have $s = \dfrac{1}{1-u}$ and so the function f must be defined by

$$f(u) = \frac{1}{1-u}.$$

Finally, we see that the generating function for the process satisfying the initial conditions must be given by

$$s\{G(s, t)\}^\alpha = 1 \bigg/ \left\{1 - \frac{(s-1)(1+\alpha\lambda t)}{s}\right\}.$$

Simplifying and solving for G, we have

$$G(s, t) = (1+\alpha\lambda t)^{-\frac{1}{\alpha}}\left(1 - \frac{\alpha\lambda t s}{1+\alpha\lambda t}\right)^{-\frac{1}{\alpha}},$$

and expanding this in powers of s and identifying the co-efficient of s^x, we see that

$$P_x(t) = (1+\alpha\lambda t)^{-\frac{1}{\alpha}}\left(\frac{\alpha\lambda t}{1+\alpha\lambda t}\right)^x\left(\frac{\frac{1}{\alpha}(\frac{1}{\alpha}+1)\ldots(\frac{1}{\alpha}+x-1)}{x!}\right)$$

$$= \frac{\lambda^x t^x}{x!}(1+\alpha\lambda t)^{-\frac{1}{\alpha}-x}\prod_{i=0}^{x-1}(1+i\alpha), \quad x = 0, 1, 2, \ldots.$$

By taking the limit of this expression for $P_x(t)$ as $\alpha \to 0$ it will be observed that this particular limiting form of the Polya process is the Poisson process with parameter λ.

For those processes in which an explicit expression for $G(s, t)$ has been derived, by applying the results of §14 the two fundamental properties (the arithmetic mean and the variance of x at time t) are given by

$$\mu(t) = \frac{\partial G(1, t)}{\partial s},$$

$$\sigma^2(t) = \frac{\partial^2 G(1, t)}{\partial s^2} + \frac{\partial G(1, t)}{\partial s} - \left\{\frac{\partial G(1, t)}{\partial s}\right\}^2.$$

§66. Birth and death process. A process which is useful as a model of queues and other practical situations is the birth and death process which again deals with population size but where the population is now subject both to increases of the pure birth process type and decreases of the pure death process type. Attention is restricted to the case in which the conditional probabilities of changes are independent of time.

When there are x members in the population at time t,

(i) the conditional probability of one addition to the population in $(t, t+\delta t)$ is $\lambda_x \delta t + o(\delta t)$;

(ii) the conditional probability of one death in the population in $(t, t+\delta t)$ is $\mu_x \delta t + o(\delta t)$;

(iii) the conditional probabilities of more than one birth, of more than one death, and of one birth together with one death in $(t, t+\delta t)$ are all $o(\delta t)$.

Setting up the recurrence equations for $P_x(t)$ in the usual way we find that

$$P_0'(t) = \mu_1 P_1(t) - (\mu_0 + \lambda_0)P_0(t),$$

$$P_x'(t) = \mu_{x+1}P_{x+1}(t) - (\mu_x + \lambda_x)P_x(t) + \lambda_{x-1}P_{x-1}(t), \quad x \geqslant 1.$$

The commonest case is the linear birth and death process for which $\lambda_x = x\lambda$ and $\mu_x = x\mu$, where λ and μ are constants. This clearly arises when members of the population act independently and each has probability $\lambda\delta t + o(\delta t)$ of producing one birth and probability $\mu\delta t + o(\delta t)$ of dying in $(t, t+\delta t)$ if alive at time t.

Substituting these values, introducing $G(s, t) = \sum_{x=0}^{\infty} P_x(t)s^x$ and following the method of previous sections we find that

$$\frac{\partial G}{\partial t} - (\lambda s - \mu)(s-1)\frac{\partial G}{\partial s} = 0.$$

Solving this by standard methods and taking the initial condition to be that there is originally one member of the population it follows that

$$G(s, t) = \frac{\mu(1 - e^{-t(\lambda-\mu)}) - (\mu - \lambda e^{-t(\lambda-\mu)})s}{\lambda - \mu e^{-t(\lambda-\mu)} - \lambda(1 - e^{-t(\lambda-\mu)})s}.$$

The value of $P_x(t)$ is given by the coefficient of s^x in this expansion and can be expressed in the form

$$P_0(t) = \alpha(t), \quad P_x(t) = \{1 - \alpha(t)\}\{1 - \beta(t)\}\{\beta(t)\}^{x-1}, \quad x \geqslant 1$$

where $\alpha(t) = \dfrac{\mu(e^{(\lambda-\mu)t} - 1)}{\lambda e^{(\lambda-\mu)t} - \mu}$ and $\beta(t) = \dfrac{\lambda(e^{(\lambda-\mu)t} - 1)}{\lambda e^{(\lambda-\mu)t} - \mu}$.

Differentiating $G(s, t)$ with respect to s and putting $s = 1$ the arithmetic mean of the population size at time t is seen to be $e^{(\lambda-\mu)t}$. From this it follows that as $t \to \infty$ the mean population size tends to 0, 1 or ∞ according as $\mu > \lambda$, $\mu = \lambda$ or $\mu < \lambda$.

The variance of the population size at time t is found to be

$$\frac{\lambda+\mu}{\lambda-\mu}e^{(\lambda-\mu)t}\{e^{(\lambda-\mu)t}-1\}$$

and the probability of extinction by time t, which is $P_0(t) = \alpha(t)$, is found to tend to the limit 1 or μ/λ as $t \to \infty$ according as $\lambda \leqslant \mu$ or $\lambda > \mu$.

The birth and death model applies also to populations which are subject to increases and decreases in numbers due to immigration and emigration. Supposing that there is a probability, independent of time and of population size, $\kappa\delta t+o(\delta t)$ of one addition to the population due to immigration in $(t, t+\delta t)$ then this can be allowed for by including κ as part of λ_x. Similarly the emigration effect can be incorporated in μ_x.

§67. Applications of the birth and death process.

The type of population described by a birth and death process takes many different forms in practice. Several examples will illustrate the generality of the model.

(i) Suppose that the population consists of the number of occupied lines in a telephone exchange assumed to have an infinite number of lines available. This could be an approximation to an exchange with a finite number of lines subject to a low intensity of incoming calls and is not an unrealistic theoretical situation. If it is assumed that incoming calls arrive in a Poisson pattern with parameter λ, i.e., the probability of a new call in $(t, t+\delta t)$ is $\lambda\delta t+o(\delta t)$, and that calls in operation each have independent probability $\mu\delta t+o(\delta t)$ of being completed in $(t, t+\delta t)$, then it is clear that the behaviour of the system is governed by the birth and death process in which x denotes the number of lines occupied and $\lambda_x = \lambda$, $\mu_x = x\mu$.

If the number of available lines were not infinite but some finite number k, and if incoming calls arriving when all lines were occupied were held in a queue to await lines, then with the same assumptions as above regarding probabilities of incoming calls and completion of calls, a birth and death process again describes the system. Now x must be defined as the total of the number of lines occupied and the number of calls being held awaiting free lines, and $\lambda_x = \lambda$ while $\mu_x = x\mu$ for $0 \leqslant x \leqslant k$ and $\mu_x = k\mu$ for $x > k$.

(ii) Industrial management is often faced with the problem of analysing losses due to breakdown of machinery and the design of the most economical arrangements for repair. A birth and death process is applicable to the following situation. Suppose a group of k identical machines is under the care of one mechanic. If the probability that any machine in operation at time t breaks down in $(t, t+\delta t)$ is $\lambda\delta t + o(\delta t)$, if machines act independently, if the probability that a machine being serviced at t returns to service in $(t, t+\delta t)$ is $\mu\delta t + o(\delta t)$ and if machines requiring repair form a queue as necessary, then taking x to be the total number of machines out of action, it is seen that x is governed by the birth and death process for which

$$\lambda_x = (k-x)\lambda, \quad 0 \leqslant x \leqslant k,$$
$$\mu_x = \mu, \quad 1 \leqslant x \leqslant k,$$
$$\mu_0 = 0.$$

From such a model, it is possible to build up a picture of the average time a machine breaking down will have to wait for service and also the proportion of time the mechanic will not be occupied. Similar properties can be examined for the model based on the assumption of two mechanics being allocated to the group of machines and thus a decision as to whether the salary of the second mechanic is more than covered by the consequent reduction in the cost of wasted machine time can be reached.

(iii) Simple queueing systems from a variety of practical fields can be treated by an appropriate birth and death process. In the typical simple queueing system a new arrival requiring service arrives in $(t, t+\delta t)$ with probability $\lambda \delta t + o(\delta t)$, service to a customer being served at time t ends in $(t, t+\delta t)$ with probability $\mu \delta t + o(\delta t)$ and consequently when there is a single server of the queue, if x denotes the number in the queue including the individual being served, x is governed by the birth and death process with

$$
\begin{aligned}
\lambda_x &= \lambda, && 0 \leqslant x < \infty, \\
\mu_x &= \mu, && 1 \leqslant x < \infty, \\
\mu_0 &= 0.
\end{aligned}
$$

Corresponding models can be set up for queues with more than one source of service. These queues may consist of shop customers, hospital out-patients, aircraft waiting for landing space, etc., and it is obvious that the analysis of the properties of such systems is of great practical importance.

§68. Limiting distributions for Markov processes.

For most processes the feature of fundamental interest is whether as $t \to \infty$ the probability distribution $\{P_x(t)\}$ tends to a limiting distribution $\{\pi_x\}$. One way to investigate this property is to find the explicit solution $\{P_x(t)\}$ and see whether the individual probabilities tend to limiting values as $t \to \infty$. However it is not always easy to identify the values $P_x(t)$, even in cases for which a limiting distribution does exist, and it is usually preferable to adopt an alternative approach. It is clear that whenever the limiting distribution does exist, it must still satisfy the fundamental recurrence relations for the process together with the additional property that $\frac{\partial}{\partial t} \pi_x = 0$, and consequently $\frac{\partial}{\partial t} G(s) = 0$ where $G(s) = \sum\limits_{x=0}^{\infty} \pi_x s^x$ and so is the limit as $t \to \infty$ of $G(s, t)$. The use of this property considerably simplifies the solution of the recurrence equations. Markov's theorem which establishes the existence of limiting distributions for a certain class of processes will be established in the next section. Before doing this, however, it is instructive to examine the application of the two suggested methods of identifying the limiting distribution in a particular example.

If x denotes the number of lines in use in a telephone exchange with an infinite number of available lines and if incoming calls and the completion of existing calls are governed by the probabilities given in §67 (i) then it is known that x behaves according to the birth and death process with $\lambda_x = \lambda$ and $\mu_x = x\mu$. The probabilities $P_x(t)$ are then known to satisfy

$$P_0'(t) = \mu P_1(t) - \lambda P_0(t),$$

$$P_x'(t) = (x+1)\mu P_{x+1}(t) - (x\mu + \lambda)P_x(t) + \lambda P_{x-1}(t), \quad x \geqslant 1,$$

and the generating function $G(s, t) = \sum\limits_{x=0}^{\infty} P_x(t)s^x$, must satisfy

$$\frac{\partial G}{\partial t} + \mu(s-1)\frac{\partial G}{\partial s} = \lambda(s-1)G.$$

Solving this by standard methods and introducing the initial condition that $P_0(0) = 1$ we find that

$$G(s, t) = \exp\left\{\frac{\lambda}{\mu}[(s-1)(1-e^{-\mu t})]\right\}.$$

From this, by identifying the coefficient of s^x, it follows that

$$P_x(t) = (\lambda/\mu)^x(1-e^{-\mu t})^x \exp(-\lambda(1-e^{-\mu t})/\mu)/x!.$$

Now since $\mu > 0$, $e^{-\mu t} \to 0$ as $t \to \infty$ and so

$$\underset{t\to\infty}{Lt}\, P_x(t) = e^{-\lambda/\mu}(\lambda/\mu)^x/x!$$

whence it follows that x has a limiting distribution, of Poisson type, as $t \to \infty$.

The alternative approach requires the prior assumption of the existence of a limiting distribution $\{\pi_x\}$ as the limit of $\{P_x(t)\}$ as $t \to \infty$. If this exists, the corresponding probability generating function $G(s) = \sum_{x=0}^{\infty} \pi_x s^x$ is found to satisfy a first order ordinary differential equation. This is obtained by observing that the limiting probabilities must satisfy the simpler recurrence equations

$$0 = -\lambda\pi_0 + \mu\pi_1,$$

$$0 = -\lambda\pi_x - x\mu\pi_x + \lambda\pi_{x-1} + (x+1)\mu\pi_{x+1}, \quad x \geqslant 1,$$

from which it follows that

$$-\lambda G - s\mu\frac{dG}{ds} + \lambda sG + \mu\frac{dG}{ds} = 0.$$

Solving this and using the condition $G(1) = \sum_{x=0}^{\infty} \pi_x = 1$ it is seen that

$$G(s) = e^{-\lambda(1-s)/\mu},$$

whence π_x can be identified as $e^{-\lambda/\mu}(\lambda/\mu)^x/x!$.

Thus the values of $\{\pi_x\}$ found by the two methods are the same. The first method which did not require any prior assumption of the existence of the limiting distribution entailed more elaborate analysis. Before using the alternative second method which is generally simpler, it is necessary to ascertain that the limiting distribution exists.

§69. Markov's Theorem on limiting distributions.

It is first necessary to define transition probabilities for Markov processes analogous to those for Markov chains. The term $P_{ij}(t)$ denotes the probability that $x = i$ at time t conditional on $x = j$ at time 0; we note that $\sum_i P_{ij}(t) = 1$ for all j. Thus the probability $P_x(t)$ can be expressed in the form

$$P_x(t) = \sum_i P_i(0)P_{xi}(t)$$

where the summation extends over all possible states of the system. It is also clear that

$$P_{xk}(t+\tau) = \sum_i P_{ik}(t)P_{xi}(\tau).$$

Since $\sum_i P_i(0) = 1$, the value of $P_x(t)$ will tend to a limit π_x as $t \to \infty$, whenever $P_{xi}(t) \to \pi_x$, which is independent of i, and it is with the behaviour of $P_{xi}(t)$ that Markov's theorem is concerned.

The applicability of the theorem is restricted to processes

for which x is a discrete variate with only a finite number of possible values; these can be taken as $x = 0, 1, \ldots, n$, where n is finite. It is further restricted to processes which are transitive. A process is **transitive** if for all i, j satisfying $0 \leqslant i \leqslant n, 0 \leqslant j \leqslant n$ there exists a finite time t for which $P_{ij}(t) > 0$. In descriptive terms this means that a process is transitive whenever it is possible for a transition to take place from one value of x to any other value of x.

Markov's theorem. For any transitive Markov process with a finite number of states, as $t \to \infty$ the transition probability $P_{xi}(t)$ tends to a limit π_x which is independent of i.

To establish the result, define

$$M_x(t) = \max_{0 \leqslant i \leqslant n} P_{xi}(t), \quad m_x(t) = \min_{0 \leqslant i \leqslant n} P_{xi}(t).$$

Then since

$$P_{xi}(t+\tau) = \sum_{r=0}^{n} P_{ri}(\tau)P_{xr}(t) \leqslant M_x(t) \sum_{r=0}^{n} P_{ri}(\tau) = M_x(t)$$

it follows that $M_x(t+\tau) \leqslant M_x(t)$; that is to say $M_x(t)$ is a monotonic non-increasing function of t. Similarly $m_x(t)$ is a monotonic non-decreasing function of t and hence as $t \to \infty$ both $M_x(t)$ and $m_x(t)$ must tend to limits. The theorem will be established if we can prove that as $t \to \infty$,

$$\Delta_x(t) = M_x(t) - m_x(t) \to 0.$$

Since the process is transitive, for $0 \leqslant i \leqslant n$ and $0 \leqslant r \leqslant n$ there must exist a time t_0 such that $P_{ri}(t_0) > 0$. Define

$$d_{il}^r = P_{ri}(t_0) - P_{rl}(t_0), \quad 0 \leqslant i, l, r \leqslant n,$$

and define $\sum_{r} {}_+ d_{il}^r$ to be the sum of all positive d_{il}^r for any given i, l and $\sum_{r} {}_- d_{il}^r$ to be the sum of all negative d_{il}^r.

Then since

$$\sum_r P_{ri}(t_0) = \sum_r P_{rl}(t_0) = 1, \quad 0 \leqslant i, l \leqslant n,$$

it follows that

$$\sum_r d_{il}^r = 0 = \sum_+ \left| d_{il}^r \right| - \sum_- \left| d_{il}^r \right|,$$

and hence that

$$\sum_+ \left| d_{il}^r \right| = \sum_- \left| d_{il}^r \right| = h_{il}, \quad 0 \leqslant i, l \leqslant n.$$

Now since $P_{rl}(t_0) > 0$, for $0 \leqslant l, r \leqslant n$,

$$h_{il} = \sum_+ d_{il}^r =$$
$$\sum_+ \{P_{ri}(t_0) - P_{rl}(t_0)\} < \sum_+ P_{ri}(t_0) \leqslant \sum_r P_{ri}(t_0) = 1,$$

and since this inequality holds for all $0 \leqslant i, l \leqslant n$ it follows that

$$h = \max h_{il} < 1.$$

If q is any positive number then

$$P_{xi}(qt_0 + t_0) - P_{xl}(qt_0 + t_0)$$
$$= \sum_r P_{ri}(t_0) P_{xr}(qt_0) - \sum_r P_{rl}(t_0) P_{xr}(qt_0)$$
$$= \sum_r \{P_{ri}(t_0) - P_{rl}(t_0)\} P_{xr}(qt_0)$$
$$= \sum_r d_{il}^r P_{xr}(qt_0)$$
$$= \sum_+ d_{il}^r P_{xr}(qt_0) - \sum_- \left| d_{il}^r \right| P_{xr}(qt_0)$$
$$\leqslant M_x(qt_0) h_{il} - m_x(qt_0) h_{il}$$
$$= h_{il} \Delta_x(qt_0)$$
$$\leqslant h \Delta_x(qt_0).$$

P Q

This inequality being true for any $0 \leqslant i, l \leqslant n$, the values of i and l can be selected so that

$$P_{xi}(qt_0 + t_0) = M_x(qt_0 + t_0)$$

and

$$P_{xl}(qt_0 + t_0) = m_x(qt_0 + t_0),$$

and substituting these in the above inequality we have

$$\Delta_x(qt_0 + t_0) = M_x(qt_0 + t_0) - m_x(qt_0 + t_0) \leqslant h\Delta_x(qt_0).$$

Successive application of this result shows that

$$\Delta_x(qt_0 + t_0) \leqslant h^q \Delta_x(t_0),$$

and since $\Delta_x(t_0)$ is the difference between two probabilities it cannot exceed unity; so

$$\Delta_x(qt_0 + t_0) \leqslant h^q.$$

Now since $h < 1$ the right-hand side tends to zero as $q \to \infty$, and so it follows that $\Delta_x(t) \to 0$ as $t \to \infty$ which proves the theorem.

§70. Queues. An aspect of stochastic processes with many practical applications is the analysis of queueing systems. Such a system is governed by four properties:

(i) the input distribution which gives the probability function for inter-arrival times between successive "new customers";

(ii) the queue discipline which states the order in which a number of waiting customers will be served; usually there is first-come first-served discipline, but there are special cases with varying types of priorities;

(iii) the number of service points;

(iv) the service time distribution which defines the

probability function for the length of time to serve one customer.

Attention will be confined to those systems in which all inter-arrival times of successive customers are identically distributed and are independent of one another, of the existing queue length and of the service times. Likewise service times will be identically distributed and independent of queue length and arrival times. Finally only systems with first-come first-served discipline will be considered.

In §62 it was shown that whenever there was probability $\lambda \delta t + o(\delta t)$ of a specified event happening in $(t, t + \delta t)$ the time elapsing until the first occurrence had continuous probability function $\lambda e^{-\lambda t}$. Thus if there is a queueing system with independent inter-arrival times with input probability density function $\lambda e^{-\lambda t}$, a single server with service time governed by the independent probability density function $\mu e^{-\mu t}$, and if $x(t)$ denotes the number of "customers" in the queue at time t including the one being served, it is clear that the behaviour of $x(t)$ conforms to the birth and death process with $\lambda_x = \lambda$ for $x \geqslant 0$, $\mu_0 = 0$, and $\mu_x = \mu$ for $x \geqslant 1$. The generalisation to multi-server systems can be described by a corresponding birth and death process by making suitable modifications to the values of μ_x.

These queueing models have been found to provide realistic representations of the conditions of congestion at telephone exchanges and in shops. By taking other input and service-time distributions, models can be set up to describe other practical queueing systems such as the arrival of patients for treatment at hospital out-patient departments and the arrival of ships with cargo to be unloaded. Complications arise in the mathematical analysis of such systems since the birth and death process is no longer applicable, and the special type of Markov dependence does not hold. In §73 a method of examining certain of these more general systems is described.

In all queueing systems, practical interest centres on the limiting distribution of queue size as $t \to \infty$, and §§71 and 72 examine this problem for the two basic queueing processes associated with telephone exchange traffic.

§71. Queueing systems with loss.

Consider the problem of determining the limiting probability distribution of the number of occupied lines in a telephone exchange which has a finite number, k, of lines. Calls arrive with probability $\lambda \delta t + o(\delta t)$ of a new call being added to the system in $(t, t+\delta t)$ provided all lines are not already occupied; the probability of multiple arrivals in $(t, t+\delta t)$ is $o(\delta t)$. In a system with loss, it is assumed that any incoming call arriving when all lines are occupied is lost, that is to say the call is cancelled, and, unlike the system to be described in §72, is not held in some sort of queue to await the clearing of a line. Each line occupied at time t has independent probability $\mu \delta t + o(\delta t)$ of being cleared in $(t, t+\delta t)$. If $x(t)$ denotes the number of lines occupied at time t, it follows that the behaviour of $x(t)$ is given by the birth and death process for which

$$\begin{aligned}
\lambda_x &= \lambda, \qquad 0 \leqslant x < k, \\
\lambda_x &= 0, \qquad x = k, \\
\mu_x &= x\mu, \qquad 0 \leqslant x \leqslant k,
\end{aligned}$$

and where, of course, x can only take the values $0, 1, 2, \ldots, k$.

What is now required is the determination of $\{\pi_x\}$, the limiting form of $\{P_x(t)\}$ as $t \to \infty$, if it can be established that such a limiting distribution exists. To find an explicit expression for $P_x(t)$ is difficult and the problem is more conveniently tackled by the second method of §68. Since the behaviour of x is governed by a Markov process with a finite number of states which is clearly transitive, the theorem of §69 establishes the existence of a limiting distribution $\{\pi_x\}$. The limiting probabilities must satisfy the recurrence equations for $\{P_x(t)\}$ with $P'_x(t) = 0$ and these are found to be

$$-\lambda\pi_0 + \mu\pi_1 = 0,$$
$$\lambda\pi_{x-1} - (\lambda + x\mu)\pi_x + (x+1)\mu\pi_{x+1} = 0, \quad 0 < x < k,$$
$$\lambda\pi_{k-1} - k\mu\pi_k = 0,$$

and there is also the additional normalising condition $\sum_{x=0}^{k} \pi_x = 1$.

To solve this system of linear equations define

$$z_x = \lambda\pi_{x-1} - x\mu\pi_x, \quad 1 \leqslant x \leqslant k.$$

The equations are then seen to be

$$z_1 = 0,$$
$$z_x - z_{x+1} = 0, \qquad\qquad 1 \leqslant x < k,$$
$$z_k = 0,$$

whence is follows that

$$z_x = 0 \qquad\qquad 1 \leqslant x \leqslant k.$$

Hence for $1 \leqslant x \leqslant k$,

$$\pi_x = \frac{\lambda}{\mu x}\pi_{x-1} = \frac{\lambda^2}{\mu^2 x(x-1)}\pi_{x-2} = \ldots = \frac{\lambda^x}{\mu^x x!}\pi_0.$$

Now since $\sum\limits_{x=0}^{k} \pi_x = 1$, the value of π_0 must be given by

$$\pi_0 = \frac{1}{\sum\limits_{x=0}^{k} \left(\frac{\lambda}{\mu}\right)^x \Big/ x!},$$

so that finally

$$\pi_x = \frac{\left(\frac{\lambda}{\mu}\right)^x \Big/ x!}{\sum\limits_{x=0}^{k} \left(\frac{\lambda}{\mu}\right)^x \Big/ x!}, \qquad 0 \leqslant x \leqslant k.$$

These expressions for $\{\pi_x\}$ are known as Erlang's formulae after the Danish mathematician A. K. Erlang who was a pioneer in the mathematical investigation of traffic problems in telephone systems.

From the practical point of view, the important limiting property of a system with loss is the probability that an incoming call will fail to find a free line and hence be lost. The limiting value of this probability must be π_k, the probability that all lines are occupied, and an evaluation of this is necessary in any critical examination of the practical efficiency of the system.

§72. **Queueing systems with waiting.** If the system of §71 is modified to allow waiting, that is if incoming calls which arrive when all lines are occupied are held in rotation to await free lines, then $x(t)$, the total number of occupied lines together with any calls being held, conforms to the birth and death process with

$$\lambda_x = \lambda, \qquad 0 \leqslant x < \infty,$$
$$\mu_x = x\mu, \qquad 0 \leqslant x \leqslant k,$$
$$\mu_x = k\mu, \qquad x > k.$$

The two properties of interest are the limiting probability of an incoming call having to wait, and the limiting probability distribution which governs the length of time elapsing until a call, which has to wait, can be connected to a clear line, first-come first-served discipline being assumed.

Since $x(t)$ can now take an infinity of possible values, Markov's theorem can no longer be applied to justify the existence of a limiting distribution, $\{\pi_x\}$, as $t \to \infty$. The alternative approach of §68 of finding an explicit form for $\{P_x(t)\}$ and examining its limit as $t \to \infty$ is not convenient to apply to this particular process. It has been established, however, that the limiting distribution does exist provided that $\lambda < k\mu$, and this result will be assumed without justification here.

The limiting probabilities π_x must satisfy the recurrence relations

$$-\lambda\pi_0 + \mu\pi_1 = 0,$$
$$\lambda\pi_{x-1} - (\lambda + x\mu)\pi_x + (x+1)\mu\pi_{x+1} = 0, \qquad 0 < x < k,$$
$$\lambda\pi_{x-1} - (\lambda + k\mu)\pi_x + k\mu\pi_{x+1} = 0, \qquad x \geqslant k,$$

together with the usual normalising condition

$$\sum_{x=0}^{\infty} \pi_x = 1.$$

Defining

$$z_x = \lambda\pi_{x-1} - x\mu\pi_x, \qquad 1 \leqslant x \leqslant k,$$

it follows, as in §71, that

$$z_x = 0, \qquad 1 \leqslant x \leqslant k.$$

If $\alpha = \lambda/\mu$ then for $0 \leqslant x \leqslant k$ we have

$$\pi_x = \frac{\alpha^x}{x!}\pi_0,$$

and in particular

$$\pi_k = \frac{\alpha^k}{k!}\pi_0.$$

For $x \geqslant k$ the recurrence relation can be written in the form

$$k\mu(\pi_{x+1}-\pi_x) = \lambda(\pi_x-\pi_{x-1}),$$

and summation over the values $x = k,\ k+1,\ k+2,\ \dots,$ $k+r$ gives

$$k\mu(\pi_{k+r+1}-\pi_k) = \lambda(\pi_{k+r}-\pi_{k-1}),$$
$$k\mu\pi_{k+r+1}+(\lambda\pi_{k-1}-k\mu\pi_k) = \lambda\pi_{k+r},$$
$$k\mu\pi_{k+r+1}+z_k = \lambda\pi_{k+r}.$$

Since $z_k = 0$, this shows that

$$\pi_{k+r+1} = \frac{\alpha}{k}\pi_{k+r}, \qquad r \geqslant 0,$$

and hence that

$$\pi_{k+r+1} = \left(\frac{\alpha}{k}\right)^{r+1}\pi_k = \left(\frac{\alpha}{k}\right)^{r+1}\frac{\alpha^k}{k!}\pi_0.$$

Thus the limiting distribution $\{\pi_x\}$ is given by

$$\pi_x = \frac{\alpha^x}{x!}\pi_0, \qquad 0 \leqslant x \leqslant k,$$

$$\pi_x = \frac{\alpha^x}{k!}\frac{\pi_0}{k^{x-k}}, \qquad x > k,$$

where

$$\frac{1}{\pi_0} = \sum_{x=0}^{k-1}\frac{\alpha^x}{x!} + \frac{k^k}{k!}\sum_{x=k}^{\infty}\left(\frac{\alpha}{k}\right)^x$$

$$= \sum_{x=0}^{k-1}\frac{\alpha^x}{x!} + \frac{k^k}{k!}\left(\frac{\alpha}{k}\right)^k \frac{1}{1-\frac{\alpha}{k}} \qquad \text{provided } \frac{\alpha}{k} < 1.$$

Thus

$$\frac{1}{\pi_0} = \sum_{x=0}^{k-1}\frac{\alpha^x}{x!} + \frac{\alpha^k}{(k-\alpha)(k-1)!}.$$

We note that the condition for convergence is $\lambda < k\mu$ which general considerations also would suggest as being necessary for the existence of a limiting distribution.

If π denotes the limiting probability of an incoming call having to wait it is clear that

$$\pi = \sum_{x=k}^{\infty}\pi_x = \frac{k^k}{k!}\pi_0\sum_{x=k}^{\infty}\left(\frac{\alpha}{k}\right)^x = \frac{\alpha^k\pi_0}{(k-\alpha)(k-1)!}.$$

It is now possible to determine, for the limiting distribution, the probability, $P(w > t)$, that an incoming call has to wait for at least time t to obtain a clear line. Let $P_x(w > t)$ denote the conditional probability that an incoming call has to wait for at least time t if the number of lines occupied and calls being held is x when that call arrives. Then

$$P(w > t) = \sum_{x=0}^{\infty} \pi_x P_x(w > t),$$

but since $P_x(w > t) = 0$ whenever $x < k$, there then being no waiting, we have

$$P(w > t) = \sum_{x=k}^{\infty} \pi_x P_x(w > t).$$

The remaining step is the evaluation of the conditional probabilities $P_x(w > t)$ for $x \geqslant k$.

Consider $P_{k+r}(w > t)$ which is the probability that a call which arrives to find all lines full and r previous calls waiting will have to wait for at least time t to obtain a free line. The required free line will become available when a total of $(r+1)$ lines have been freed and consequently $P_{k+r}(w > t)$ must be equal to the probability of not more than r lines being cleared in time t.

If $p_i(t)$ denotes the probability of exactly i lines being freed in time t, then $P_{k+r}(w > t) = \sum_{i=0}^{r} p_i(t)$. Now throughout the period of waiting all lines are occupied and the probability of a line being freed in $(t, t+\delta t)$ is $k\mu\delta t + o(\delta t)$, so that the number of lines freed in total time t must be governed by the Poisson process with parameter $k\mu$. From this it follows that

$$p_i(t) = e^{-k\mu t} \frac{(k\mu t)^i}{i!}$$

for all values of i, so that

$$P_{k+r}(w > t) = \sum_{i=0}^{r} e^{-k\mu t} \frac{(k\mu t)^i}{i!}.$$

Thus finally

$$P(w > t) = \sum_{x=k}^{\infty} \pi_x \left\{ \sum_{i=0}^{x-k} e^{-k\mu t} \frac{(k\mu t)^i}{i!} \right\}$$

$$= e^{-k\mu t} \sum_{x=k}^{\infty} \left(\frac{\alpha}{k}\right)^{x-k} \pi_k \sum_{i=0}^{x-k} \frac{(k\mu t)^i}{i!}$$

$$= \pi_k e^{-k\mu t} \sum_{i=0}^{\infty} \frac{(k\mu t)^i}{i!} \sum_{x=k+i}^{\infty} \left(\frac{\alpha}{k}\right)^{x-k}$$

$$= \pi_k e^{-k\mu t} \sum_{i=0}^{\infty} \frac{(k\mu t\alpha)^i}{k^i i!} \sum_{x=k+i}^{\infty} \left(\frac{\alpha}{k}\right)^{x-k-i}$$

$$= \pi_k e^{-k\mu t} \sum_{i=0}^{\infty} \frac{(\lambda t)^i}{i!} \left\{ 1 + \frac{\alpha}{k} + \frac{\alpha^2}{k^2} + \ldots \right\}$$

$$= \frac{\pi_k e^{-k\mu t} e^{\lambda t}}{1 - \alpha/k}.$$

Now $\pi_k = \dfrac{\alpha^k}{k!} \pi_0 = \pi(1 - \alpha/k)$, and so

$$P(w > t) = \pi e^{-(k\mu - \lambda)t}, \qquad t \geqslant 0.$$

Thus the waiting time w has a conditional limiting distribution of negative exponential type with parameter $k\mu - \lambda$; this again shows that unless $\lambda < k\mu$ no limiting distribution can exist.

The probability of waiting is $P(w > 0)$ and this is seen to be π, the value already obtained.

§73. Single server queues with general service time distribution.

The queues considered so far have been specialised in that their inter-arrival times and service times were independent continuous variates with negative exponential distributions. It is due to this property that the Markov dependence holds for $x(t)$, the queue length at time t, and the birth and death process model is applicable. Whenever arrival times or service times conform to other distributions an alternative approach is necessary to examine the behaviour of $x(t)$.

We now examine single-server queues with first-come first-served discipline for which inter-arrival times have the negative exponential probability function $\lambda e^{-\lambda t}$, that is to say the probability of a new arrival in $(t, t+\delta t)$ is $\lambda \delta t + o(\delta t)$, and general service time probability function $\phi(t)$. It is not possible to examine the behaviour of $x(t)$ for general finite time t, but it is possible to discuss the limiting behaviour of $\{P_x(t)\}$, namely $\{\pi_x\}$, as $t \to \infty$. This is done by restricting attention to an enumerable set of times $t_1, t_2, t_3, \ldots$ and examining an embedded Markov chain.

If the behaviour of the queue length $x(t)$ is examined only at the enumerable points in time $t_1, t_2, t_3, \ldots$ which correspond to the times at which service is completed for respectively the first, the second, the third, ... customer, then the behaviour of $x(t)$ at these points is given by a Markov chain with constant transition probabilities. It has been shown that with inter-arrival probability function $\lambda e^{-\lambda t}$ the probability of exactly j arrivals during time t is given by $e^{-\lambda t}(\lambda t)^j/j!$ for $j = 0, 1, 2, \ldots$.

Now consider the queue lengths at the times of departure of two successive customers say rth and $(r+1)$th. These queue lengths will include the respective customers whose service times are about to start but, of course, must exclude the customers just leaving. If E_k denotes the state of the system when the queue length is k, then the required transition probabilities are

$$p_{jk} = p(E_j \text{ at } t_{r+1} \mid E_k \text{ at } t_r).$$

If $k > 0$, $t_{r+1} - t_r$ must be the service time of the $(r+1)$th customer which has probability function $\phi(t)$. Starting with queue length k at t_r, to end with queue length j at t_{r+1} remembering that the $(r+1)$th customer leaves, it is seen that in the interval $t_{r+1} - t_r$ there must be exactly $j+1-k$ new arrivals. The probability that $t_{r+1} - t_r$ lies in $(t, t+dt)$ is $\phi(t)dt$ and the conditional probability of $(j+1-k)$ arrivals in this interval is $\dfrac{e^{-\lambda t}(\lambda t)^{j+1-k}}{(j+1-k)!}$ for $j+1-k \geqslant 0$, and zero for $j+1-k < 0$.

Thus for $k > 0$,

$$p_{jk} = \int_0^\infty \frac{e^{-\lambda t}(\lambda t)^{j+1-k}}{(j+1-k)!}\, \phi(t)dt \quad \text{for } j \geqslant k-1,$$

$$p_{jk} = 0, \text{ for } j < k-1.$$

When $k = 0$, no customer is waiting for service after the rth customer leaves. In this case $t_{r+1} - t_r$ consists of the time which elapses until the next customer arrives, say τ_{r+1}, together with the service time t of this customer which again must have probability function $\phi(t)$. The length of the queue at t_{r+1} after the $(r+1)$th customer leaves is given by the number of arrivals during the service time portion t of $t_{r+1} - t_r$ so that the transition probabilities are now given by

$$p_{j0} = \int_0^\infty \frac{e^{-\lambda t}(\lambda t)^j}{j!}\, \phi(t)dt, \quad j \geqslant 0.$$

If, for simplicity, $\displaystyle\int_0^\infty \frac{e^{-\lambda t}(\lambda t)^j}{j!}\, \phi(t)dt$ is denoted by q_j, the transition probabilities can be written in the form

$$p_{jk} = q_{j+1-k}, \qquad k \geqslant 1, \qquad j \geqslant k-1,$$
$$p_{j0} = q_j, \qquad\qquad j \geqslant 0,$$
$$p_{jk} = 0, \qquad\qquad j < k-1.$$

If the embedded Markov chain has a limiting distribution $\{\pi_j\}$ as $r \to \infty$, that is as $t_r \to \infty$, then these limiting probabilities must satisfy the equations

$$\pi_j = \sum_i p_{ji}\pi_i, \quad j \geqslant 0,$$

which in this case can be expressed as

$$\pi_0 = q_0\pi_0 + q_0\pi_1,$$
$$\pi_1 = q_1\pi_0 + q_1\pi_1 + q_0\pi_2,$$
$$\pi_2 = q_2\pi_0 + q_2\pi_1 + q_1\pi_2 + q_0\pi_3,$$
$$\cdot \quad \cdot \quad \cdot \quad \cdot \quad \cdot \quad \cdot \quad \cdot \quad \cdot \quad \cdot \quad \cdot \quad \cdot \quad \cdot$$

together with

$$\sum_{j=0}^{\infty} \pi_j = 1.$$

On multiplying these recurrence equations respectively by $1, s, s^2, \ldots$, and summing and defining $G(s) = \sum_{j=0}^{\infty} \pi_j s^j$ as the limiting probability generating function, it follows that

$$G(s) = \{q_0 + sq_1 + s^2 q_2 + \ldots\} \{\pi_0 + \pi_1 + \pi_2 s + \pi_3 s^2 + \ldots\}$$

$$= \left\{ \sum_{j=0}^{\infty} \int_0^{\infty} e^{-\lambda t} \frac{(\lambda t)^j s^j}{j!} \phi(t) dt \right\} \left\{ \pi_0 + \frac{G(s) - \pi_0}{s} \right\}$$

$$= \int_0^{\infty} e^{-\lambda t} \left\{ \sum_{j=0}^{\infty} \frac{(\lambda t s)^j}{j!} \right\} \phi(t) dt \left\{ \pi_0 + \frac{G(s) - \pi_0}{s} \right\}.$$

Hence

$$sG(s) = \left\{ \int_0^\infty e^{-\lambda(1-s)t} \phi(t)dt \right\} \{G(s) - \pi_0(1-s)\}$$

$$= \left\{ 1 - \lambda(1-s)\alpha_1 + \frac{\lambda^2(1-s)^2}{2!}\alpha_2 \ldots \right\} \{G(s) - \pi_0(1-s)\},$$

where $\alpha_i = \int_0^\infty t^i \phi(t)dt = E(t^i) = i$th moment of the service time distribution.

Hence

$$(s-1)\, G(s) = -\lambda\alpha_1(1-s)\, G(s) - \pi_0(1-s)$$
$$+ \text{terms in higher powers of } (1-s).$$

Now divide throughout by $s-1$, take the limiting values as $s \to 1$ and use the fact that $G(1) = \sum_{j=0}^{\infty} \pi_j = 1$ to obtain

$$\pi_0 = 1 - \lambda\alpha_1.$$

Since π_0 is a probability it follows that $\lambda\alpha_1 \leqslant 1$ for this result to have any practical meaning; thus for the limiting distribution to exist, $\lambda\alpha_1 \leqslant 1$. Now if $\lambda\alpha_1 = 1$, $\pi_0 = 0$ which means that E_0 has infinite mean recurrence time which means in turn that a limiting distribution cannot exist. Thus for a limiting distribution, $\lambda\alpha_1 < 1$ when $\pi_0 = 1 - \lambda\alpha_1$ and $G(s)$ is given by

$$G(s) = \frac{(1-\lambda\alpha_1)Q(s)}{1 - \dfrac{1-Q(s)}{1-s}} = \frac{(1-s)\,(1-\lambda\alpha_1)Q(s)}{Q(s) - s},$$

where

$$Q(s) = \sum_{j=0}^{\infty} q_j s^j = \int_0^{\infty} e^{-\lambda(1-s)t} \phi(t) dt = \sum_{j=0}^{\infty} \frac{(s-1)^j \lambda^j}{j!} \alpha_j,$$

that is to say $Q(s)$ is obtained from the moments, or moment generating function of the service time distribution.

The limiting behaviour of the embedded Markov chain after an infinite number of customers have been served must also describe the state of the queue after an infinite time interval, and so the general limiting behaviour of the queue as $t \to \infty$ can be examined by this method.

§74. Some limiting properties of queues.

Assuming the existence of a limiting distribution of queue length for the process described in §73 it is possible to establish, by elementary methods, expressions for the limiting values of average queue length and average waiting time for new customers.

Suppose that initially there are q_0 customers in the queue, that service is about to commence for the first customer and that further customers arriving will be numbered $q_0 + 1$, $q_0 + 2$, ... Let q_n denote the number of customers in the queue at the moment when service of customer number n is completed, and let a_n denote the number of new arrivals during the service time of customer number n.

Since the service times are independent identically distributed variates with continuous probability function $\phi(t)$ and arrivals are of Poisson type with parameter λ, it follows that a_1, a_2, . . . are identically distributed independent discrete variates with probability function given by

$$p(a_n = k) = \int_0^\infty \frac{e^{-\lambda t}(\lambda t)^k}{k!}\phi(t)dt, \quad k = 0, 1, 2, \ldots.$$

Each a_n has probability generating function

$$A(s) = \sum_{k=0}^\infty p(a_n = k)s^k = \int_0^\infty e^{\lambda(s-1)t}\phi(t)dt,$$

whence, by differentiating r times with respect to s and evaluating the resulting expression when $s = 1$, it follows that

$$\left[\frac{d^r A(s)}{ds^r}\right]_{s=1} = E[a_n(a_n-1)(a_n-2)\ldots(a_n-r+1)]$$

$$= \lambda^r \int_0^\infty t^r \phi(t)dt = \lambda^r \alpha_r,$$

where α_r is the rth moment of the service time distribution. The expression on the left-hand side is seen to be the rth factorial moment of a_n so that

rth factorial moment of $a_n = \mu'_{(r)}(a_n) = \lambda^r \alpha_r$.

In particular,

$$\mu'_{(1)}(a_n) = E(a_n) = \lambda\alpha_1,$$

$$\mu'_{(2)}(a_n) = E[a_n(a_n-1)] = \lambda^2\alpha_2,$$

and from these it follows that

$$\sigma^2(a_n) = \lambda\alpha_1 + \lambda^2(\alpha_2 - \alpha_1^2) = \lambda\alpha_1 + \lambda^2\sigma_\alpha^2,$$

where σ_α^2 denotes the variance of the service time distribution.

For the arrival distribution of this queueing system, the

P R

mean inter-arrival time is $\int_0^\infty \lambda t e^{-\lambda t} dt = \dfrac{1}{\lambda}$, and the mean service time is α_1. Defining the **traffic intensity** of any system to be

$$\rho = \frac{\text{mean service time}}{\text{mean inter-arrival time}},$$

this system is seen to have $\rho = \lambda \alpha_1$. The ratio of the standard deviation of any variate to its arithmetic mean is known as the fractional coefficient of variation, C, and we denote the fractional coefficient of variation of the service time distribution by C_α which is seen to be $\dfrac{\sigma_\alpha}{\alpha_1}$.

Thus the arithmetic mean and the variance of a_n can be expressed in the form

$$\mu_1'(a_n) = \rho, \quad \sigma^2(a_n) = \rho + \rho^2 C_\alpha^2 \quad \text{for all } n \geqslant 1.$$

It is obvious that

$$q_{n+1} = q_n - 1 + a_{n+1} \quad \text{when } q_n > 0,$$

and

$$q_{n+1} = a_{n+1} \quad \text{when } q_n = 0.$$

Introducing Heaviside's Unit Function $U(x)$ which satisfies

$$U(x) = \begin{cases} 1, & x > 0, \\ 0, & x \leqslant 0, \end{cases}$$

we see that the equations for q_{n+1} can be written in the form of the single equation

$$q_{n+1} = q_n - U(q_n) + a_{n+1}.$$

Taking the average, or expected values of all terms in this equation,

$$E(q_{n+1}) = E(q_n) - E U(q_n) + E(a_{n+1}),$$

and, with a limiting distribution for q_n, $E(q_{n+1})$ must equal $E(q_n)$ so that

$$E U(q_n) = E(a_{n+1}) = \rho.$$

Now

$$E U(q_n) = 1 \times p(q_n > 0) + 0 \times p(q_n = 0)$$

and thus

$$p(q_n > 0) = \rho \text{ and } p(q_n = 0) = 1 - \rho.$$

This means that in the stationary state the probability that a customer on completion of service leaves no one else waiting for service is $1 - \rho$, and this is also the probability that a customer arrives to find no queue waiting and consequently receives immediate service.

Squaring the equation for q_{n+1} and observing that $q_n U(q_n) = q_n$ and $U^2(q_n) = U(q_n)$, we have

$$q_{n+1}^2 = q_n^2 + U(q_n) + a_{n+1}^2 + 2 q_n a_{n+1} - 2 a_{n+1} U(q_n) - 2 q_n.$$

Now taking expected values and using the fact that a_{n+1} is independent of q_n and hence also of $U(q_n)$, together with the stationary property $E(q_n^2) = E(q_{n+1}^2)$,

$$2E(q_n) = E U(q_n) + E(a_{n+1}^2) \\ + 2E(q_n) E(a_{n+1}) - 2E(a_{n+1}) E U(q_n),$$

$$2E(q_n)\{1 - E(a_{n+1})\} = \rho + \rho + \rho^2 C_\alpha^2 + \rho^2 - 2\rho^2,$$

$$E(q_n) = \rho + \frac{\rho^2(1 + C_\alpha^2)}{2(1 - \rho)}.$$

From this expression for $E(q_n)$ it is seen that the expected queue length can be reduced for given mean service time

P R*

by reducing the variability of the service time and hence C_α. For example

$$\phi(t) = \frac{1}{\alpha_1} e^{-t/\alpha_1}, \quad 0 \leqslant t \leqslant \infty, \quad E(t) = \alpha_1,$$

$$\sigma(t) = \alpha_1, \quad C_\alpha = 1, \quad E(q_n) = \frac{\rho}{1-\rho};$$

$$\phi(t) = \frac{4t}{\alpha_1^2} e^{-2t/\alpha_1}, \quad 0 \leqslant t \leqslant \infty, \quad E(t) = \alpha_1,$$

$$\sigma(t) = \frac{\alpha_1}{\sqrt{2}}, \quad C_\alpha = \frac{1}{\sqrt{2}}, \quad E(q_n) = \frac{\rho(1-\frac{1}{4}\rho)}{1-\rho};$$

$$\phi(t) = \begin{cases} 1, & t = \alpha_1, \\ 0, & t \neq \alpha_1, \end{cases} \qquad E(t) = \alpha_1,$$

$$\sigma(t) = 0, \quad C_\alpha = 0, \quad E(q_n) = \frac{\rho(1-\frac{1}{2}\rho)}{1-\rho};$$

showing that constant service time distribution reduces the average queue length for the corresponding exponential service time distribution in the ratio of $(1-\frac{1}{2}\rho)$. For small values of ρ, this reduction is not appreciable but for such queues the average queue length is never large. For limiting distributions to exist $\rho < 1$ so that the greatest reduction in $E(q_n)$ produced for constant against exponential service time is $\underset{\rho \to 1}{\mathrm{Lt}} (1-\frac{1}{2}\rho) = \frac{1}{2}$. This feature is important in designing service systems to reduce average queue length even if it is impossible to reduce average service time.

From the value of $E(q_n)$ it is possible to deduce the average waiting time of a customer from time of arrival to completion of service. If w_n is the waiting time of the nth customer, since on completion of his service he leaves behind q_n members of a queue subject to first-come first-served discipline then q_n must be the number of customers arriving in time w_n. With Poisson type arrivals it follows that

$$E(q_n) = \lambda E(w_n),$$

and thus

$$E(w_n) = \frac{1}{\lambda} \left\{ \rho + \frac{\rho^2(1+C_\alpha^2)}{2(1-\rho)} \right\},$$

or, since $\lambda \alpha_1 = \rho$,

$$\frac{E(w_n)}{\alpha_1} = 1 + \frac{\rho(1+C_\alpha^2)}{2(1-\rho)}.$$

This is known as Pollaczek's formula, and is of fundamental importance in analysing and designing single server queueing systems.

EXERCISES VIII

1. The probability that a fisherman catches one fish in the time interval $(t, t+\delta t)$ is $2\delta t + o(\delta t)$; the probability that he catches more than one fish in this time interval is $o(\delta t)$. Show that the probability that exactly x fish are caught in the interval $(0, t)$ is

$$\mathrm{e}^{-2t} \frac{(2t)^x}{x!}, \qquad x = 0, 1, 2, \ldots .$$

If $\tau_1, \tau_2, \ldots, \tau_n, \ldots$ denote the times, measured from zero, at which fish are caught, find the probability function for τ_1.

Prove that the distribution function for τ_n, the total time which elapses before the nth fish is caught, is given by

$$F_n(t) = p\{\tau_n \leqslant t\} = 1 - \sum_{j=1}^{n-1} e^{-2t}\frac{(2t)^j}{j!}, \quad t \geqslant 0,$$

$$F_n(t) = 0, \qquad\qquad\qquad t < 0,$$

and find the probability function for τ_n.

2. The probability that a machine breaks down in the time interval $(t, t+\delta t)$ is $\lambda\delta t + o(\delta t)$. Prove that the probability density function of the time which elapses before the first breakdown is $\lambda e^{-\lambda t}$ where $0 \leqslant t \leqslant \infty$.

The independent probability density functions for the times until machines A, B, C have their first breakdown are respectively $\lambda e^{-\lambda t}$, $\mu e^{-\mu t}$, $v e^{-vt}$ where in each case $0 \leqslant t \leqslant \infty$. Prove that the probability density function for the time which elapses until the first breakdown of any machine is $(\lambda+\mu+v)e^{-(\lambda+\mu+v)t}$ and deduce the mean time until the first breakdown.

Prove that the probability that the three machines have their first breakdowns in the order A, B, C is

$$\frac{\lambda\mu}{(\mu+v)(\lambda+\mu+v)}.$$

3. The conditional probability of a birth in $(t, t+\delta t)$ when there are n members in the population at time t is $(\lambda+\mu n)\delta t + o(\delta t)$ where $\lambda > 0$, $\mu > 0$. The probability of multiple births in $(t, t+\delta t)$ is $o(\delta t)$ and there are no deaths.

If initially there were no members of the population find the probability function for the number of members of the population at time t and obtain the arithmetic mean and the variance of this distribution.

4. A population, subject to change by birth, death and immigration, contains $x(t)$ members at time t. The conditional probability of a member of the population, alive at time t, giving birth to another member in $(t, t+\delta t)$ is $\lambda \delta t + o(\delta t)$; the conditional probability of a member, alive at time t, dying in $(t, t+\delta t)$ is $\mu \delta t + o(\delta t)$; the probability that one immigrant joins the population in $(t, t+\delta t)$ is $\varepsilon \delta t + o(\delta t)$ and the probability of more than one change in population size in $(t, t+\delta t)$ is $o(\delta t)$.

If $P_x(t)$ denotes the probability that the population consists of x members at time t, and $G(s, t) = \sum\limits_{x=0}^{\infty} P_x(t)s^x$, show that

$$\frac{\partial G(s,t)}{\partial t} = (\lambda s - \mu)(s-1)\frac{\partial G(s,t)}{\partial s} + \varepsilon(s-1)G(s,t).$$

If $x(0) = 0$ and $\lambda = \mu = 1$, find $G(s, t)$ and hence find the arithmetic mean and the variance of the population size at time t.

5. A population initially has no members. When there are x members at time t, the conditional probability that there should be one member added in $(t, t+\delta t)$ is $\lambda_x(t)\delta t + o(\delta t)$ and the conditional probability of more than one additional member in $(t, t+\delta t)$ is $o(\delta t)$. The population suffers no decrements. The probability of x members at time t is $P_x(t)$.

Show that

$$\begin{aligned} P_0'(t) &= -\lambda_0(t)P_0(t), \\ P_x'(t) &= \lambda_{x-1}(t)P_{x-1}(t) - \lambda_x(t)P_x(t), \quad x \geqslant 1, \end{aligned}$$

and hence prove that when $\lambda_x(t) = \dfrac{1+\alpha x}{1+\alpha t}$ where α is a positive constant,

$$P_0(t) = (1+\alpha t)^{-\frac{1}{\alpha}},$$

$$P_x(t) = \frac{t^x}{x!}(1+\alpha t)^{-\frac{1}{\alpha}-x}\prod_{i=0}^{x-1}(1+i\alpha), \quad x \geqslant 1.$$

Prove that the mean and the variance of population size at time t are respectively t and $t(1+\alpha t)$.

Obtain the probability density function for the time which elapses before the first member appears in the population and the conditional probability density function for the time which elapses between the appearances of the first and second members when the first appears at time τ.

6. A group of m machines is serviced by a single workman. When a machine breaks down it is serviced immediately unless the workman is already servicing another machine, in which case a waiting line is formed. For each machine in use at time t there is independent probability $\lambda\delta t + o(\delta t)$ that it breaks down in the time interval $(t, t+\delta t)$. A machine being serviced at time t has probability $\mu\delta t + o(\delta t)$ of returning to use in the time interval $(t, t+\delta t)$.

The system is in state E_n if n machines are out of action. If $P_n(t)$ denotes the probability of E_n at time t prove that

$$P_0'(t) = -m\lambda P_0(t) + \mu P_1(t),$$
$$P_n'(t) = -\{(m-n)\lambda + \mu\}P_n(t) + (m-n+1)\lambda P_{n-1}(t)$$
$$+ \mu P_{n+1}(t), \quad 1 \leqslant n \leqslant m-1,$$
$$P_m'(t) = -\mu P_m(t) + \lambda P_{m-1}(t).$$

Hence show that if $\{P_n(t)\} \rightarrow \{\pi_n\}$ as $t \rightarrow \infty$, the limiting probabilities satisfy

$$m\lambda\pi_0 = \mu\pi_1,$$
$$\{(m-n)\lambda+\mu\}\pi_n = (m-n+1)\lambda\pi_{n-1}+\mu\pi_{n+1},$$
$$1 \leqslant n \leqslant m-1,$$
$$\mu\pi_m = \lambda\pi_{m-1}$$

and obtain their values.

If w denotes the average number of machines in the waiting line, excluding the machine being serviced, prove that

$$w = m-\frac{\lambda+\mu}{\lambda}(1-\pi_0).$$

7. If a population consists of n members at time t, there is probability $\lambda_n\delta t+o(\delta t)$ of a member being added and probability $\mu_n\delta t+o(\delta t)$ of a member being removed in $(t, t+\delta t)$, the probability of multiple changes in the population in this interval being negligible. If $P_n(t)$ denotes the probability that there are n members at time t, prove that

$$P_0'(t) = \mu_1 P_1(t)-(\lambda_0+\mu_0)P_0(t),$$
$$P_n'(t) = \lambda_{n-1}P_{n-1}(t)+\mu_{n+1}P_{n+1}(t)-(\lambda_n+\mu_n)P_n(t), \quad n > 0.$$

Show that if $\lambda_n = n\lambda$ and $\mu_n = n(n-1)\mu$ then $G(s, t) = \sum_{n=0}^{\infty} P_n(t)s^n$ satisfies the partial differential equation

$$\frac{\partial G}{\partial t} = s(s-1)\left\{\lambda\frac{\partial G}{\partial s} - \mu\frac{\partial^2 G}{\partial s^2}\right\}.$$

If $\{P_n(t)\}$ tends to the limiting distribution $\{\pi_n\}$ and $G(s) = \sum_{n=0}^{\infty} \pi_n s^n$ deduce that

$$\lambda\frac{\partial G}{\partial s} = \mu\frac{\partial^2 G}{\partial s^2}$$

and hence find $\{\pi_n\}$ given that $\pi_0 = 0$.

8. Cars arrive independently, according to a Poisson process with parameter λ, at a car park which has space for N cars. When the car park is full new arrivals do not wait.

Cars leave the park independently and the probability that any car in the park at time t leaves in the time interval $(t, t+\delta t)$ is $\lambda\delta t + o(\delta t)$. Obtain the differential-difference equations for the probabilities $P_n(t)$ of finding n spaces occupied at time t.

Obtain the limiting probability distribution as $t \to \infty$, and hence find the limiting probability that a car, on arrival, will be unable to find parking space.

9. A shop employs k assistants to serve customers. Any assistant who is serving a customer at time t has probability $\mu\delta t + o(\delta t)$ of completing service in the time interval $(t, t+\delta t)$. When there is at least one assistant free at time t, the probability of one additional customer in $(t, t+\delta t)$ is $\lambda\delta t + o(\delta t)$, the probability of multiple arrivals in that interval being $o(\delta t)$; when all assistants are serving at time t the probability of any new customer arriving in $(t, t+\delta t)$ is zero.

Find the limiting probability distribution as $t \to \infty$ for the number of customers being served. If $\lambda = \mu$ and $k = 3$ find the limiting probability that all assistants are occupied and the average number of assistants occupied.

10. Customers arrive at random with density λ at a single-server queue with first-come first-served discipline. Service times are independently distributed with the negative exponential probability density function

$$\phi(t) = \mu e^{-\mu t}, \quad 0 \leqslant t \leqslant \infty.$$

The size of the queue, including the customer being served, is restricted to m customers, so that potential customers who arrive to find a queue of length m do not join it. If $\mu > \lambda$ and $\rho = \lambda/\mu$, show that the limiting probability that there are x customers in the queue is

$$\frac{\rho^x(1-\rho)}{1-\rho^{m+1}}, \qquad x = 0, 1, 2, \ldots, m.$$

Hence find the mean equilibrium queue length.

Of a very large number, N, of potential customers arriving at the queue, how many actually join the queue and how many are served immediately? What is the expected waiting time of a customer who joins the queue?

11. A telephone exchange has k channels. Calls arrive at random with density $\lambda = 2$. When all lines are occupied, calls are held in rotation to await empty channels. If all conversation lengths independently follow the negative exponential distribution with probability function

$$\phi(t) = 3\mathrm{e}^{-3t}, \quad 0 \leqslant t \leqslant \infty,$$

find the difference equations satisfied by the limiting probabilities $\{\pi_i\}$, where π_i denotes the probability that the total of occupied lines and calls being held is i. Hence obtain the limiting probability that an incoming call will have to wait.

If w denotes the time an incoming call has to wait for an empty channel prove that in the limiting distribution

$$p(w > t) = \pi\mathrm{e}^{-(3k-2)t}, \quad 0 \leqslant t \leqslant \infty,$$

where π is the limiting probability of having to wait at all.

If originally $k = 2$, examine the improvement in (i) the probability of having to wait and (ii) the probability of having to wait more than $t = 5$, if an extra channel is introduced.

12. A shop has five serving assistants. Customers arrive at random at the rate of one per unit time. When all assistants are busy, customers form a queue to await service in rotation. If all service times independently follow the negative exponential distribution

$$\phi(t) = \tfrac{2}{5}e^{-2t/5}, \quad 0 \leqslant t \leqslant \infty,$$

find the limiting probability, as $t \to \infty$, that a customer will have to queue before receiving service.

If w denotes the time that a customer queues before service, prove that in the limiting distribution

$$p(w > t) = \pi e^{-t}, \quad 0 \leqslant t \leqslant \infty,$$

where π is the limiting probability of having to wait for service.

13. The arrivals of customers at a shop with a single server is according to a Poisson process with parameter λ. When the server is free he immediately starts attending an arriving customer; when the server is busy a newcomer must wait until all previous customers have been served. If all service times are independent of one another and of the arrival times of customers and have common probability density function

$$\phi(t) = te^{-t}, \quad 0 \leqslant t \leqslant \infty,$$

find the transition probabilities for the embedded Markov chain.

Hence find the recurrence equations satisfied by the limiting probability distribution $\{\pi_i\}$ where π_i denotes the limiting probability, as time tends to infinity, that there are i customers waiting including the one being served.

Prove that the probability generating function for this limiting distribution is

$$F(s) = \frac{1-2\lambda}{1-2\lambda s + \lambda^2 (s-1)s},$$

and hence show that $\lambda < \frac{1}{2}$ if the limiting distribution exists.

14. The input of a single-server queue is according to a Poisson process with parameter λ. The service discipline is first-come first-served and the service times are independent of one another and of the arrival times and have common probability density function

$$\phi(t) = \frac{1}{\Gamma(k)} \frac{k}{\alpha} \left(\frac{kt}{\alpha}\right)^{k-1} e^{-kt/\alpha}, \quad 0 \leqslant t \leqslant \infty.$$

Find the transition probabilities for the embedded Markov chain.

Hence, assuming the existence of a limiting probability distribution $\{\pi_i\}$, where π_i denotes the probability, as time tends to infinity, that there are i customers in the queue, obtain the probability generating function $F(s) = \sum_{i=0}^{\infty} \pi_i s^i$, and show that the limiting distribution cannot exist unless $\lambda\alpha < 1$.

Find the mean queue length when the system has reached a stationary condition.

15. Customers arrive at random with density λ in a single-server queueing system with first-come first-served discipline and independent service times with probability density function

$$\phi(x) = \frac{1}{6}x^3 e^{-x}, \quad 0 \leqslant x \leqslant \infty.$$

If at time zero there are q_0 customers in the queue and service to the first is about to start, if q_n denotes the number of customers in the queue at the moment of termination of service and departure of the nth customer and if ξ_n denotes the number of customers arriving during the service of the nth customer, prove that the rth factorial moment of ξ_n is $\frac{1}{6}\lambda^r(r+3)!$

Assuming that a limiting distribution exists for q_n as $n \to \infty$, prove that in the limit

$$E(q_n) = \frac{2\lambda(2-3\lambda)}{1-4\lambda},$$

and that in the limit the expected waiting time of the nth customer is

$$\frac{2(2-3\lambda)}{1-4\lambda}.$$

ANSWERS TO EXERCISES

1. $\frac{3}{16}, \frac{3}{8}, \frac{11}{16}$. 2. $\frac{3}{32}, \frac{1}{4}$. 3. $\frac{3}{16}$. 4. $\frac{1}{8}$. 5. $\frac{1}{7}$.

6. $\frac{1}{5}$. 7. $\frac{1}{20}, \frac{7}{220}, (3n^2 - 3n + 1)/\{n(6n-1)(6n-2)\}$.

8. $\frac{1}{66}, 53/(100 \times 49 \times 33)$. 9. $3255/(120)^3$.

10. $36/143, 101/143$. 11. $\frac{1}{2}$. 12. $\frac{2}{3}$. 13. $\frac{2}{3}$.

14. $2/(n+1), \frac{1}{9}$. 15. $4 + 2\sqrt{2}$. 16. $\frac{1}{2}k^2, 1 - \frac{1}{2}(2-k)^2$.

17. $\frac{11}{36}, \frac{7}{36}, \frac{1}{6}$. 18. $\frac{7}{16}, \frac{1}{6}, \frac{1}{18}$. 19. $\frac{4}{9}$.

20. $3 \log_e 2 - 2$. 21. $\frac{3}{4}, 127/128$. 22. $\frac{3}{5}$.

23. $1 - \{1 - (\frac{3}{5})^3\}^3 = 0 \cdot 518$. 24. $832/2401$.

25. $p_n = (\frac{1}{2})^n \{1 - (\frac{4}{5})^n\}$. 26. $80/243, 256/729, 233/729$.

27. $992/3125, 432/3125$. 28. $497/2592$. 29. $r/(r+g)$.

30. $p^2(1 + 2q + 3q^2), p^2(1+q)/(1-pq)$. 31. $189/625$,
    $856/10^4, 5$. 32. $20p^3q^3, p^4(1 + 5q + 15q^2), p^2/(1 - 2pq)$.

33. $\frac{1}{4}, \frac{11}{24}, \frac{1}{4}, \frac{1}{24}, 84876/(24)^5$. 34. $\frac{11}{36}, \frac{5}{36}, \frac{1}{6}, \frac{24}{29}, \frac{5}{29}$.

35. More probable. 36. $365 . 364 \ldots (366 - n)/(365)^n, 23$.

37. $319/324, 61/81$. 38. $5/34$.

39. $q = p/(1-p), r = p(1-2p), p = \frac{1}{3}$ gives equal probabilities; for other permissible values of p the probability of B winning is reduced.

40. $39/64, 4/5, 7921/16\,384$. 41. $\frac{4}{7}, \frac{5}{12}$.

42. $27/256, 27/175, 9/37$. 43. $27/65, 51/65, 5/14$.

44. $3/25$. 45. $20/21, 68/81$. 46. $\frac{1}{5}, \frac{9}{25}, \frac{10}{39}$.

47. $\frac{1}{6}, \frac{1}{4}, \frac{7}{9}, \frac{2}{3}$. 48. $101/200, 2/101, 103/202, 2^n/(99 + 2^n)$,
    11. 49. $1/3d$. 50. $4, 4/81$. 51. $0 \cdot 146, 0 \cdot 187$.

52. $(\frac{4}{6})^n, (\frac{2}{3})^n - (\frac{1}{2})^n$.

53. $1 - 4(\frac{3}{4})^n + 6(\frac{1}{2})^n - 4(\frac{1}{4})^n, (\frac{3}{4})^{n-1} - 3(\frac{1}{2})^{n-1} + 3(\frac{1}{4})^{n-1}$.

54. $\{6^{10} - 6 \times 5^{10} + 15 \times 4^{10} - 20 \times 3^{10} + 15 \times 2^{10} - 6\}/6^{10}$,
$\{15 \times 4^{10} - 60 \times 3^{10} + 90 \times 2^{10} - 60\}/6^{10}$,
$\{6^{10} - 20 \times 3^{10} + 45 \times 2^{10} - 36\}/6^{10}$.

55. $\{8^8 - 7^8 - 6^8 - 3^8 + 5^8 + 2^8 + 1\}/8^8$
$8^2\{7^5 + 2 \times 6^5 + 5 \times 3^5 - 3 \times 5^5 - 6 \times 2^5 - 7\}/$
$\{8^8 - 7^8 - 6^8 - 3^8 + 5^8 + 2^8 + 1\}$.

56. $\{9^8 + 8^8 - 6^8 - 5^8 + 4^8\}/10^8$,
$\{7^8 + 6^8 + 5^8 - 3 \times 4^8\}/\{9^8 + 8^8 - 6^8 - 5^8 + 4^8\}$.

57. $\dfrac{1}{2!} - \dfrac{1}{3!} + \dfrac{1}{4!} - \dfrac{1}{5!} + \dfrac{1}{6!}$, 265.

58. $\left\{\dfrac{1}{2!} - \dfrac{1}{3!} + \ldots + (-1)^r \dfrac{1}{r!}\right\}\Big/ (n-r)!$.

59. $\{8^{12} - 8 \times 7^{12} + 28 \times 6^{12} - 56 \times 5^{12} + 70 \times 4^{12} - 56 \times 3^{12}$
$+ 28 \times 2^{12} - 8\}/8^{12}$,
$\{28 \times 6^{12} - 168 \times 5^{12} + 420 \times 4^{12} - 560 \times 3^{12}$
$+ 420 \times 2^{12} - 168\}/8^{12}$.

60. $\alpha(1-\alpha)^{n-1} + 2\alpha(1-2\alpha)^{n-1} + (1-3\alpha)(3\alpha)^{n-1}$
$- 3\alpha(1-3\alpha)^{n-1} - (1-2\alpha)(2\alpha)^{n-1} - (1-\alpha)\alpha^{n-1}$.

INDEX

265